Preface

The subjects of this book—parts feeding, orientation, and mechanized assembly—are growing rapidly in importance, and, in general, universities and colleges have been lagging behind industry in the study of these important fields of production engineering technology. Whereas mechanization of the assembly process is being carried out at an increased rate in practice, the subject has only recently begun to appear in undergraduate academic courses and, up until now, few universities have studied it at the postgraduate level. As a result, formal analytical treatments of the subject in the form of research papers and articles are still quite rare and a text-book has not before been published. Now that, in the academic sphere, increasing attention is being given to the study of these subjects, it is hoped that this book will serve as a text for those studying production engineering technology in universities and colleges. It is further hoped that those engaged in engineering production itself will find the book useful in exploiting the advantages of the various techniques available.

The contents have been deliberately restricted to the fundamentals of the subject in order to provide a basic understanding of the problems involved. No attempt has been made to provide detailed designs of equipment for special tasks and the reader is referred to some of the articles listed in the bibliography for descriptions of manufactured equipment.

With those in mind who are responsible for the teaching and development of academic courses in production engineering technology, Appendix II describes two typical experiments suitable for students.

The authors are very much indebted to those with whom they have been associated during the past few years and who have assisted indirectly in the preparation of this book. They would like to thank Professor A. W. J. Chisholm for his encouragement and support of the work in mechanized assembly at the University of Salford.

G. BOOTHROYD
A. H. REDFORD

Glossary of Symbols

A	track acceleration, in/sec^2
A_b	basic cost of part, shillings
A_n	normal component of track acceleration, in/sec^2
A_0	minimum vertical bowl acceleration for feeding to occur, in/sec^2
A_p	parallel component of track acceleration, in/sec^2
A_v	vertical component of track acceleration, in/sec^2
B	constant giving rate of increase of cost due to increased quality level of parts, shillings
C	cost of part, shillings
C_a	cost of operating assembly machine to produce one acceptable assembly, shillings
C_A	depreciation rate of one automatic workhead, shillings/min
C_B	depreciation rate of one work carrier, shillings/min
C_t	total assembly costs, shillings
C_{to}	total cost of operator assembly, shillings
C_T	depreciation rate per workstation of assembly machine transfer device, shillings/min
D	down-time, per cent
D_a	depth of track, in.
D_b	base diameter of truncated cone, in.
D_h	diameter of rivet head, in.
D_t	inside diameter of tubular track, in.
F	frictional force, lbf
F_b	frictional force between part and base, lbf
F_m	machine rate, c/s
F_{max}	maximum feed rate, parts/sec
F_n	average unrestricted feed rate for nth load increment, parts/sec
F_0	mean feed rate, parts/sec
F_w	frictional force between part and wall of centrifugal hopper feeder, lbf
H	vertical height of column of parts, in.
K	factor used in analysis of free-transfer machine
L	length of track or length of slot in feeder, in.
L_n	average bowl load during nth increment of load
L_p	total number of parts placed in bowl at each refill
M	cost of operating assembly machine if only acceptable assemblies are produced, shillings/min
M_t	total operating cost of assembly machine, shillings/min
N	number of assemblies produced; normal force acting on part, lbf

Mechanized Assembly

Fundamentals of parts feeding,
orientation, and mechanized assembly

G. Boothroyd

Professor of Mechanical Engineering, University of Massachusetts, U.S.A.

A. H. Redford

Lecturer in Mechanical Engineering, University of Salford, England

McGRAW-HILL · LONDON

New York · Sydney · Toronto · Mexico · Johannesburg

Published by
McGRAW-HILL Publishing Company Limited, McGraw-Hill House
MAIDENHEAD, BERKSHIRE, ENGLAND

94058

Printed and bound in Great Britain

N_b	rotational speed of centrifugal hopper feeder base, rev/min
N_n	number of parts fed during nth increment of load
P	axial force acting on column of parts, lbf
P_a	production rate of acceptable assemblies, assemblies/min
P_m	maximum production rate, assemblies/min
P_u	production rate of unacceptable assemblies, assemblies/min
R	track radius, in.
R_b	radius from pivot to upper end of track of a centreboard hopper, in.
R_h	radius of centrifugal hopper feeder, in.
R_n	number of parts re-circulated during nth load increment
R_T	average re-circulation of parts during one load increment
S	load sensitivity, per cent
T	time taken to correct assembly machine fault, sec
T_c	time taken to dismantle one unacceptable assembly, sec
T_f	period of feeder cycle, sec
T_i	indexing period of indexing rotary disc feeder, sec
T_s	time taken for parts to slide out of slot in rotary disc feeder, sec
T_1	time taken to lift centreboard hopper blade, sec
T_2	dwell time of centreboard hopper blade, sec
W	operator's rate, shillings/min
W_p	weight of part, lbf
W_T	total cost of assembly machine operators, shillings/min
a	linear acceleration of part, in/sec^2
a_n	normal amplitude of track vibration, in.
a_0	amplitude of track vibration, in.
a_p	parallel amplitude of track vibration, in.
a_s	distance between adjacent slots of an external gate hopper, in.
$a_1, a_2, a_3 \ldots$	
$(a_n - 1)$	numbers of assemblies in buffer stocks
b	buffer stock
c	clearance in tubular feed track, in.
d	diameter of part or part head, in.
d_t	top diameter of truncated cone, in.
$d_1, d_2, d_3 \ldots$	
d_n	down-time on assembly machine workheads, sec
f	frequency of vibration, c/s
f_b	frequency of centreboard hopper blade cycle, c/s
g	acceleration due to gravity, in/sec^2
h	height of part head, in.
h_c	height of centre of gravity of part above feed track, in.
h_g	gap between cylinder and sleeve in external gate hopper, in.
h_s	step height of step orienting device, in.
l	length of part, in.
l_c	distance between centre of gravity and leading corner of part, in.
l_g	distance from underside of part head to centre of gravity of headed part, in.
m	proportion of defective parts causing a machine stoppage
m_1	mass per unit length of column of parts, lb/in.

m_p	mass of part, lb
m_t	total number of load increments between refills
n	number of automatic workheads
n_r	number of readings in sample
q	number of operations required to assemble product
s	standard deviation of sample
t	machine cycle times, sec
t_f	time taken to feed 100 parts
t_1	time taken for one load increment
t_p	time taken to deliver one part, sec
t_s	time taken for part to slide distance L, sec
v	velocity of part, in/sec
v_m	mean conveying velocity, in/sec
x	quality level of parts, per cent
x_{opt}	value of x for minimum assembly cost, per cent
z	number of possible stable orientations of part
α	inclination of feed track
α_p	angle of tilt of headed part
β	half-angle of cut-out orienting device
γ	phase angle between normal and parallel track vibrations
γ_{opt}	optimum phase angle
η	feeder efficiency, per cent
θ	track or delivery chute angle
$\ddot{\theta}$	angular acceleration of track, rad/sec^2
θ'	angle of inclination of rotary disc feeder
θ_m	maximum track angle
θ_{opt}	optimum track angle
θ_T	track angle for maximum tilt of headed part
λ	angle of inclination of external gate hopper axis
μ	effective coefficient of friction
μ_b	coefficient of dynamic friction between part and base of centrifugal hopper feeder
μ_d	coefficient of dynamic friction
μ_s	coefficient of static friction
μ_w	coefficient of dynamic friction between part and wall of centrifugal hopper feeder
ϕ	hopper wall angle
ϕ_g	angular position of gate of external gate hopper
ψ	vibration angle
ψ_{opt}	optimum vibration angle
ω	frequency of vibration, rad/sec

Contents

1.

Introduction

The increasing need for finished goods in large quantities has, in the past, led engineers to search for and to develop new methods of production. Many individual developments in the various branches of manufacturing technology have been made and have allowed the increased production of improved finished goods at lower cost. One of the most important production processes is the assembly process and this is required as soon as two or more component parts are to be brought together in order to produce the finished product.

The early history of assembly process development is closely related to the history of the development of mass-production methods. Thus, the pioneers of mass production are also the pioneers of the modern assembly process. Their new ideas and concepts have brought significant improvements in the assembly methods employed in large volume production.

However, although some branches of production engineering such as metal cutting and metal forming processes have recently been developing very rapidly, the technology of the basic assembly process has not been keeping pace. At present, in Britain and the U.S.A. more than 40 per cent of the total labour force in engineering is employed on assembly work and assembly costs often account for more than 50 per cent of the total manufacturing costs in an engineering industry. Statistical surveys also show that these figures are increasing every year.

In the past few years, some efforts have been made to reduce assembly costs by the application of mechanization and modern techniques such as resistance welding and die-casting. Success has, however, been very limited and many assembly operators are still using the same basic tools as those employed in the days of the industrial revolution.

1.1   Historical Development of the Assembly Process

In the early days of manufacturing technology, the complete assembly of a product was carried out by a single operator and often this operator also manufactured the individual component parts of the assembly. Consequently, it was necessary for him to be an expert in all the various aspects of his work and training a new operator was a long and expensive task. The scale of production was often limited by the availability of trained operators and not by the demand for the product.

In 1798, the U.S.A. needed a large supply of muskets and the Federal arsenals could not meet the demand. Because war with the French was imminent, it was not possible to obtain additional supplies from Europe. However, Eli Whitney, now recognized as one of the pioneers of mass production, offered to contract for making 10,000 muskets in 28 months. Although, in fact, it took $10\frac{1}{2}$ years to complete the contract, Whitney's novel ideas on mass production had by then been proved. The factory at New Haven, built specially for the manufacture of the muskets, contained machines for producing interchangeable parts. This reduced the skills required by the various operators and allowed significant increases in production rate. In his historic demonstration in 1801, Eli Whitney surprised his distinguished visitors by assembling musket locks from parts selected at random from a heap.

The results of Eli Whitney's work brought three main developments in manufacturing methods.

First, parts were manufactured on machines and were thus more consistent in quality than the hand-made parts. This resulted in interchangeability and simplified assembly work. Second, the accuracy of the product could be maintained at a higher standard, and third, production rates could be significantly increased.

Oliver Evans' conception of conveying material from one place to another without manual effort led eventually to further developments in assembly work. In 1783 he used three types of conveyor in an automatic flour mill which required only two operators. The first operator poured grain into a hopper and the second filled sacks with the flour produced by the mill. All the intermediate operations were carried out automatically with conveyors carrying the material from operation to operation.

The next significant contribution to the development of assembly methods was made by Elihu Root. In 1849 Elihu Root joined the company which was producing Colt 'six-shooters'. Even though at that time the various operations of assembling the component parts were quite simple he divided these operations into basic units which could be completed more quickly and with less chance of error. This gave rise to the concept—'divide the work and multiply the output'. Using this principle, assembly work was reduced to very simple basic operations and with only short periods of operator training, high efficiencies could be obtained.

Frederick Winslow Taylor was probably the first person to introduce the methods of time and motion study to manufacturing technology. The object was to save the operator's time and energy by arranging that the work and all things associated with the work were placed in the best positions for carrying out the required tasks. Taylor also discovered that any worker has an optimum speed of working which, if exceeded, results in a reduction in his overall performance.

Undoubtedly the main contributor to the development of production and assembly methods was Henry Ford. He described his principles of assembly in the following words:

'First, place the tools and the men in the sequence of the operations so that each part shall travel the least distance whilst in the process of finishing.

'Second, use work slides or some other form of carrier so that when a workman completes his operation he drops the part always in the same place which must always be the most convenient place to his hand and if possible have gravity carry the part to the next workman.

'Third, use sliding assembly lines by which the parts to be assembled are delivered at convenient intervals, spaced to make it easier to work on them.'

These principles were gradually applied in the production of the Model T Ford motor car.

The modern *assembly line* technique was first employed in the assembly of a flywheel magneto. In the original method, one operator assembled a magneto in 20 minutes. It was found that when the process was divided into 29 individual operations carried out by separate operators working at *assembly stations* spaced along an assembly line, the total assembly time was reduced to 13 minutes 10 seconds. When the height of the assembly line was raised by eight inches, the time was further reduced to 7 minutes. After further experiments to find the optimum speed of the assembly line conveyor, the time was reduced to 5 minutes, which was only one-quarter of the time taken by the original process of assembly. This result encouraged Henry Ford to utilize his system of assembly in other departments of the factory producing sub-assemblies for the motor car. This brought a continuous and rapidly increasing flow of sub-assemblies to the operators working on the main car assembly.

It was found that they could not cope with this increased flow and it soon became clear that the main assembly would also have to be carried out on an assembly line. At first, the movement of the main assemblies was achieved simply by pulling them by a rope from station to station. However, even this development produced the amazing result of a reduction in the total time of assembly from 12 hours 28 minutes to 5 hours 50 minutes.

Eventually, a power-driven endless conveyor was installed. It was flush with the floor and wide enough to accommodate a chassis. Space was provided for workers either to sit or stand whilst they carried out their operations and the conveyor moved at a speed of six feet per minute past 45 separate workstations. With the introduction of this conveyor, the total assembly time was reduced to 93 minutes.

Further improvements led to an even shorter overall assembly time and eventually a production rate of one car every ten seconds of the working day was achieved.

Although Ford's target of production had been exceeded and even though the overall quality of the product had improved considerably, the assembled products sometimes varied from the precise standards of the hand-built prototypes. Eventually a method of isolating difficulties and correcting them in advance was adopted before mass production started. The method was basically to set up a 'pilot' plant where a complete assembly line was installed, using exactly the same tools, templates, and forming devices, the same gauges, and even the same labour skills which would eventually be used for mass production. This has now become standard practice for all large assembly plants.

The type of assembly operation dealt with above is usually referred to as *operator assembly* and it is still the most widespread method of assembling mass- or large-batch-produced products. However, in certain cases more refined methods of assembly have now emerged.

As a logical extension of the basic assembly line principle, methods of replacing operators by mechanical means of assembly have been devised. Here, it is usual to attempt to replace operators with *automatic workheads* where the tasks being performed are very simple and to retain the operators for tasks which would be uneconomic to mechanize. This method of assembly is rapidly gaining popularity for mass production and is usually referred to as *mechanized assembly*.

By far the least used of the various methods of assembly is *automatic assembly*, where the product is assembled completely by machine. Although automatic assembly has often been the ultimate aim, the reasons given above for retaining operators on a mechanized assembly line explain why automatic assembly is not often realized in practice. However, many important developments in mechanized assembly have resulted from attempts to automate fully the assembly process.

1.2 Choice of Assembly Method

When considering the assembly of a product, a manufacturer has to take account of many factors which will affect the choice of assembly system. For a new product, the following considerations will generally be important:

(a) Cost of assembly;
(b) Production rate required;
(c) Availability of labour;
(d) Market life of product.

If an attempt is to be made to justify the mechanization of an existing operator assembly line then consideration has to be given to the redeployment of those operators who would become redundant. If labour is plentiful, the degree of mechanization will depend on the change in cost of assembly and the change in production rate brought about by the mechanization of the assembly line. However, it must be remembered that, in general, the capital investment in automatic machinery will have to be amortized over the market life of the product unless the machinery may be adapted to assemble a new product. It is clear that if this is not the case and the market life of the product is short, then mechanization will not generally be justifiable.

A shortage of labour may often lead a manufacturer to consider mechanized assembly when in fact it can be shown that operator assembly would be cheaper. Conversely, a manufacturer may be unable to mechanize because suitable employment cannot be found for the operators who would become redundant.

A further reason for considering mechanization in a situation where operator assembly would be more economic is on a research basis in order to gain experience in the field.

1.3   Advantages of Mechanized Assembly

Some of the advantages of mechanization are listed below:

(a) Reduction in cost of assembly;
(b) Increased productivity;
(c) A more consistent product;
(d) Removal of operators from hazardous operations.

A reduction in costs is often the main consideration and, except for the special circumstances listed above, it could be expected that mechanization would not be carried out if it was not expected to produce a reduction in costs.

Productivity in an advanced industrial country is an important measure of operating efficiency. Increased productivity, whilst not being directly beneficial to a manufacturer unless labour is scarce, is necessary to an expanding economy, since it releases manpower for other tasks. It is clear that mechanization of assembly lines will generally reduce the number of operators required and hence increase productivity.

Some of the tasks which an operator can easily perform are extremely difficult to duplicate on even the most sophisticated automatic workhead. An operator can often carry out a visual inspection of the part to be assembled and parts which are obviously defective can be discarded. Sometimes a very elaborate inspection system is required to detect even the most obviously defective part. If an attempt is made to assemble a part which appears to be acceptable but which is in fact defective, an operator, after unsuccessfully trying to complete the assembly can reject the part very quickly without a significant loss in production. In such a situation, however, unless the part has been rejected by the feeding device, an automatic workhead will probably stop and time will then be wasted locating and eliminating the fault. If a part only has a minor defect an operator may be able to complete the assembly and the resulting product may not be completely satisfactory. It is often suggested that one of the advantages of mechanized assembly is that it ensures a consistently high quality of product because the machine will fault if the parts do not conform to the required specification.

In some situations assembly by operators would be hazardous because of high temperatures, the presence of toxic substances, etc. Under these circumstances assembly by mechanical means is obviously advantageous.

A mechanized assembly machine usually consists of a transfer system for moving the assemblies from workstation to workstation, automatic workheads to perform the simple assembly operations, vacant workstations for operators to carry out the more complicated assembly operations, and inspection devices to check that the various operations have been completed successfully. The automatic workheads are either fed manually with individual or magazine-stored component parts or are supplied with parts from a hopper feeding and orienting device (often a vibratory bowl feeder) through a feed track. The workheads themselves usually consist of either a fastening device or a parts placing mechanism. Examples of these are nut and screw running heads, welding heads, riveting heads, soldering heads, push and guide placing mechanisms, and pick and place mechanisms.

In the following chapters these basic components of assembly machines will be dealt with separately and finally the overall performance and design of assembly machines will be discussed.

2.

Transfer Systems

In mechanized assembly the various individual assembly operations are generally carried out at separate workstations. For this method of assembly, a system is required for transferring the partly completed assemblies from workstation to workstation, and a means must be provided of ensuring that no relative motion exists between the assembly and the workhead whilst the operation is being carried out. As the assembly passes from station to station it is necessary that it be maintained in the required attitude. For this purpose, the assembly is usually built up on a base or *work carrier* and the machine is designed to transfer the work carrier from station to station; an example of a typical work carrier is shown in Fig. 2.1. Assembly machines are usually classified according to the system adopted for transferring the work carriers (Fig. 2.2). Thus an *in-line* assembly machine is one where the work carriers are transferred in line along a straight slideway and a *rotary* machine is one where the work carriers move in a circular path. In both types of machine the transfer of work carriers may be *continuous* or *intermittent*.

2.1 Continuous Transfer

With continuous transfer the work carriers are moving at constant speed whilst the workheads index backwards and forwards (Fig. 2.3). In this case the assembly operations are carried out during the period when the workheads are moving forward keeping pace with the work carriers; the workheads then return quickly to their initial positions, ready to repeat the operations during the next cycle. Continuous transfer systems have limited application in mechanized assembly because the workheads and associated equipment are often heavy and therefore difficult to accelerate and decelerate at the rates required. It is also often difficult under these circumstances to

8

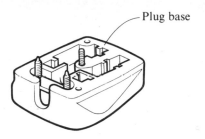

Plug base

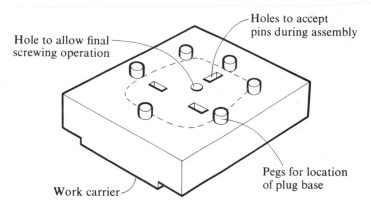

Holes to accept
pins during assembly

Hole to allow final
screwing operation

Pegs for location
of plug base

Work carrier

Figure 2.1. Work carrier suitable for holding and transferring three-pin power plug base.

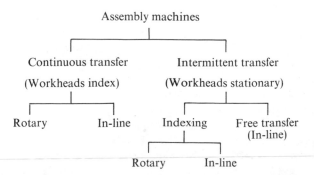

Assembly machines

Continuous transfer

(Workheads index)

Intermittent transfer

(Workheads stationary)

Rotary

In-line

Indexing

Free transfer
(In-line)

Rotary

In-line

Figure 2.2. Basic types of assembly machine.

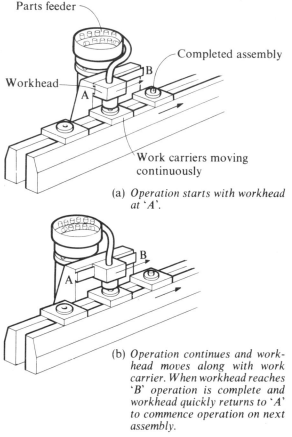

(a) *Operation starts with workhead at 'A'.*

(b) *Operation continues and workhead moves along with work carrier. When workhead reaches 'B' operation is complete and workhead quickly returns to 'A' to commence operation on next assembly.*

Figure 2.3. In-line continuous transfer machine.

maintain sufficiently accurate alignment between the workheads and work carriers during the operation cycle.

2.2   Intermittent Transfer

Intermittent transfer is the more common system employed for both rotary and in-line machines. As the name implies, the work carriers are transferred intermittently and the workheads remain stationary. Usually the transfer of all work carriers occurs simultaneously and they then remain stationary to allow time for the assembly operations. These machines may be termed *indexing* machines and typical examples of the rotary and in-line types of indexing machine are shown in Figs. 2.4 and 2.5 respectively. With the rotary indexing machine, indexing of the table brings the work carriers under the various workheads in turn, and assembly of the product is completed during one revolution of the table. Thus, at the appropriate station, a completed product may be taken from the machine after each index. The in-line indexing machine works

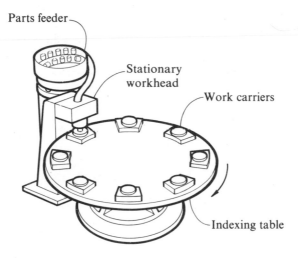

Figure 2.4. Rotary indexing machine.

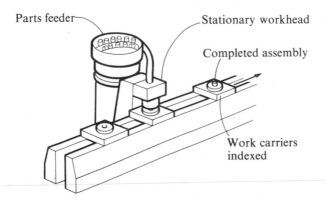

Figure 2.5. In-line indexing machine.

on a similar principle but in this case a completed product is removed from the end of the line after each index. With in-line machines provision must be made for returning the empty work carriers to the beginning of the line. The transfer mechanism on in-line machines is generally one of three types: the walking beam; the shunting work carrier; or the chain-driven work carrier.

The various stages in the operation of the walking beam are illustrated in Fig. 2.6. The mechanism consists of a fixed rail provided with grooves for location of the work carriers. A transfer rail is driven in such a way that it periodically picks up a series of work carriers and deposits them further along the fixed rail. To accomplish this, the transfer rail is attached by a linkage to a slider which is constrained to move horizontally and is activated by a piston.

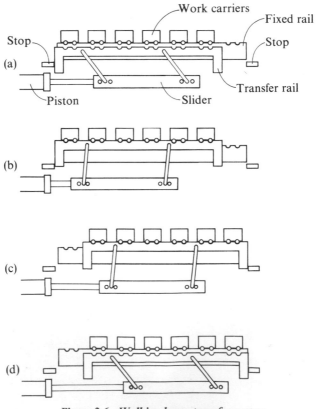

Figure 2.6. Walking beam transfer system.

Figure 2.6a shows the start of the cycle where the work carriers are resting on the fixed rail and are awaiting the next index. In Fig. 2.6b, it can be seen that as the slider moves to the left, the transfer rail will lift the work carriers from the fixed rail. At this point the supporting linkage has moved just past the vertical and is held in position by a stop. The piston now forces the slider to the right and the transfer rail and work carriers move along over the fixed rail. In the position shown in Fig. 2.6c, further motion of the slider causes the linkage to rotate anticlockwise. The transfer rail falls backward and deposits the work carriers on the fixed rail in the next index position (Fig. 2.6d). The slider then moves to the left which returns the transfer rail to its initial position. With this system work carriers reaching the end of the assembly line are returned to the beginning of the line by a suitable conveyor. With the walking beam and all other transfer devices used on in-line machines it is usual for each work carrier, after transfer, to be finally positioned and locked by a locating plunger before the assembly operation is initiated.

Another transfer system known as pawl transfer is shown in Fig. 2.7 where it can be seen that reciprocation of the transfer bar over a distance equal to the spacing of the workheads will cause the work carriers to index between the workheads.

The shunting work carrier transfer system is shown in Fig. 2.8. In this system, the work carriers have a length equal to the distance moved during one index. Positions are available for work carriers at the beginning and end of the assembly line where no assembly takes place. At the start of the cycle of operations the work carrier position at the end of the line is vacant. A mechanism pushes the queue of work carriers up to a stop at the end of the line and this indexes the work carriers one position. The piston then withdraws and the completed assembly at the end of the line is removed. The empty work carrier is lowered onto a return conveyor and the empty work carrier from the previous cycle which has been delivered by the return conveyor is raised into position at the beginning of the assembly line. Although the system described here operates in the vertical plane, the return of work carriers can also be accomplished in the horizontal plane. In this case, transfer from the assembly line to the return conveyor and vice-versa is simpler but greater floor area is used. In practice, when operating in the horizontal plane, it is more usual to dispense with the rapid return conveyor and to fit further assembly heads and associated transfer equipment in its

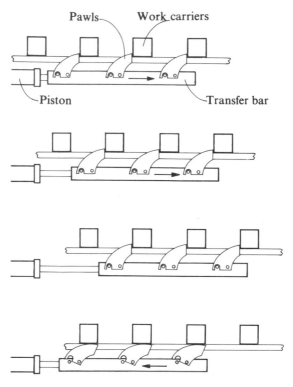

Figure 2.7. Pawl type transfer system.

place (Fig. 2.9). This system has the disadvantage that access to the various workheads may be difficult.

A further disadvantage with all shunting work carrier systems is that the work carriers themselves must be accurately manufactured. For example, if an error of $+0.001$ in. were to occur on the length of each work carrier in a 20-station machine, this would lead to an error in alignment of 0.02 in. at the last station. This could create serious difficulties in the operation of the workheads.

The chain-driven work carrier transfer system is shown in Fig. 2.10. Basically this machine uses an indexing mechanism which drives a chain to which are attached the work carriers spaced to correspond to the distance between the workheads. (An alternative to the chain drive, sometimes favoured in the U.S.A., is a flexible steel band.) With chain-driven indexing systems the problem of chain stretch must be taken into account in the design of the

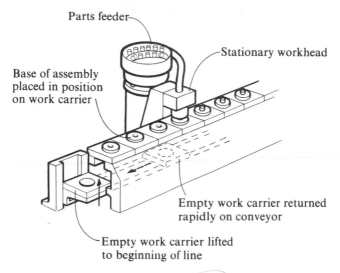

Figure 2.8. In-line transfer machine with shunting work carriers returned in vertical plane.

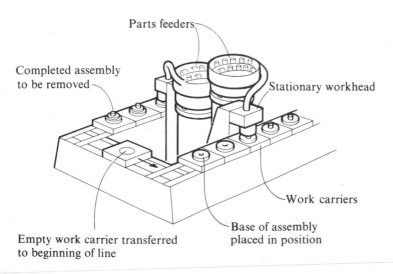

Figure 2.9. In-line transfer machine with shunting work carriers returned in horizontal plane.

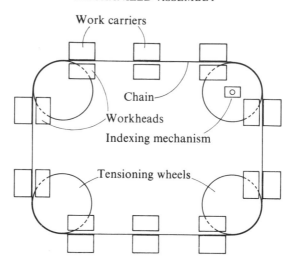

Figure 2.10. Chain-driven transfer system.

machine. Clearly, if the chain stretches, the pitching of the work carriers will vary. To overcome this fault, the usual method is to arrange for the release of the chain tension on completion of the index and to allow location plungers to position each work carrier relative to the workhead. It must be ensured that the chain does not attempt to index before the location plungers have been withdrawn.

Instead of attaching the work carriers rigidly to the chain it is possible to employ chain attachments which simply push the work carriers along guides. In this case the chain index can be arranged to leave the work carriers short of their final position, allowing location plungers to bring them into line with the workheads. With this system, chain stretch does not present a serious problem.

2.3 Indexing Mechanisms

Huby[1] lists the factors affecting the choice of indexing mechanism for an assembly machine as follows:

- (a) The required life of the machine;
- (b) The dynamic torque capacity required;
- (c) The static torque capacity required;
- (d) The power source required to drive the mechanism;
- (e) The acceleration pattern required;
- (f) The accuracy of positioning required from the indexing unit.

Generally an increase in the size of a mechanism increases its life. Experience shows which mechanisms usually give longest life for given applications and this will be dealt with later.

The dynamic torque capacity is the torque which must be supplied by the indexing unit during the index of a fully loaded machine. It is found by adding the inertia, friction, and work torques and multiplying by the life factor of the unit, the latter factor being found from experience of the use of the units.

The static torque capacity is the sum of the torques produced at the unit by the operation of the workheads. If individual location plungers are employed at each workhead then these are usually designed to withstand the forces applied by the workheads and, in this case, the static torque capacity required from the indexing unit will probably be negligible.

The power required to drive an indexing unit will be obtained from the dynamic torque applied to the unit during the machine index.

The form of the acceleration curve for the indexing unit may be very important when there is any possibility that a partially completed assembly may be disturbed during the machine index. A smooth acceleration curve will also reduce the peak dynamic torque and will thus assist the driving motor to maintain a constant speed during indexing and increase the life of the machine.

The accuracy of indexing required will not be great if locating plungers are employed to perform the final location of the work carriers or indexing table.

Various indexing mechanisms are available for use on mechanized assembly machines and typical examples are given in Figs. 2.11, 2.12, and 2.13. These mechanisms fall into two main categories; those which convert intermittent translational motion (usually provided by a piston) into angular motion by means of a rack and pinion or a ratchet and pawl (Fig. 2.11); those which are continuously driven, such as the Geneva mechanism (Fig. 2.12) or the cross-over or scroll cam shown in Fig. 2.13.

For all but very low speed indexing or very small indexing tables, the rack and pinion or ratchet and pawl mechanisms are unsuitable since they have a tendency to overshoot. The acceleration properties of both these systems are governed entirely by the acceleration pattern of the linear power source. If the power source is a pneumatic cylinder then, in order to ensure a fairly constant indexing time, it is usual to underload the cylinder, in which case the accelerations

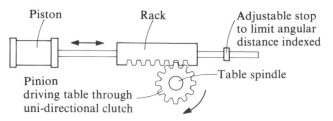

(a) *Rack and pinion with uni-directional clutch*

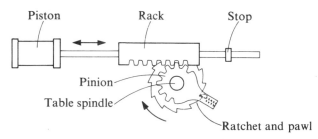

(b) *Rack and pinion with ratchet and pawl*

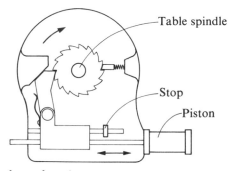

(c) *Ratchet and pawl*

Figure 2.11. Indexing mechanisms.

at the beginning and end of the stroke are very high and produce undesirable shocks.

The ratchet and pawl requires a take-up movement and must be fairly robust if it is to have a long life. The weakest point in the mechanism is usually the pawl pin and if this is not well lubricated the pawl will stick and indexing will not occur.

The Geneva type indexing mechanism has more general application in assembly machines but its cost is higher than the mechanisms

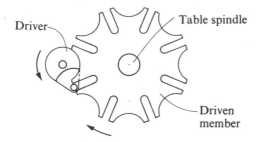

Figure 2.12. Geneva mechanism.

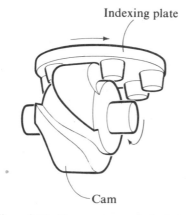

Figure 2.13. Cross-over cam indexing unit.

described above. It is capable of transmitting a high torque relative to its size and has a smooth acceleration curve. However, it has a high peak dynamic torque immediately before and after the reversal from positive to negative acceleration. In its basic form the Geneva mechanism has a fairly short life but wear can be compensated for by adjustment of the centres. The weakest point in the mechanism is the indexing pin but breakages of this part can be avoided by careful design and the avoidance of undue shock reactions from the assembly machine.

The main limitation in the use of the Geneva mechanism is its restriction in the number of stops per revolution. This is primarily due to the accelerations which occur with three-stop and more than eight-stop mechanisms.

In a Geneva mechanism, the smaller the number of stops, the greater is the adverse mechanical advantage between the driver and the driven members. This results in a high indexing velocity at the centre of the indexing movement and gives a very peaked acceleration graph. On a three-stop Geneva this peaking becomes very pronounced and since the mechanical advantage is very high at the centre of the movement, the torque applied to the index plate is greatly reduced when it is most required. The solution to these problems results in very large mechanisms relative to the output torque available.

As the number of stops provided by a Geneva mechanism increases, although the peak torque reduces, the initial and final accelerations during indexing increase. This is due to the increased difficulty of placing the driver centre close to the tangent to the indexing slot on the driven member.

For a unit running in an oil bath the clearance between the driver and driven members during the locking movement is approximately 0·001 in. To allow for wear in this region it is usual to provide a small centre-distance adjustment between the two members. The clearance established after adjustments is the main factor governing the indexing accuracy of the unit and this will generally become less accurate as the number of stops is increased. Because of the limitations in accuracy it is usual to employ a Geneva mechanism in conjunction with a location plunger and in this case a relatively cheap and accurate method of indexing is obtained.

The cross-over cam type of indexing mechanism shown in Fig. 2.13 is capable of transmitting a high torque, has a good acceleration characteristic, and is probably the most consistent and accurate form of indexing mechanism. Its cost is rather higher than the alternative mechanisms described above and it has the minor disadvantage that it is rather bulky. The acceleration characteristics are not fixed as with other types of indexing mechanism, but it can be designed to give almost any required form of acceleration curve. The normal type of cam is designed to give a modified trapezoidal form of acceleration curve which gives a low peak dynamic torque and a fairly low mean torque.

The cam can be designed to give a wide range of stops per revolution of the index plate, and the indexing is inherently accurate. A further advantage is that it always has at least two indexing pins in contact with the cam.

Figure 2.14 shows the acceleration patterns of the modified

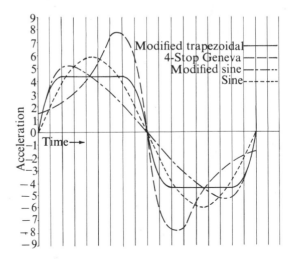

Figure 2.14. *Comparison of acceleration curves for a Geneva mechanism and various designs of cross-over cam. (After Huby[1].)*

trapezoid, sine, and modified sine cams and the Geneva mechanism for the complete index of a four-stop unit. It can be seen that the modified trapezoidal form gives the best pattern for smoothest operation and lowest peaking. The sine and modified sine both give smooth acceleration but the peak torque is increased, while with the Geneva mechanism the slight initial shock loading and the peaking at the reversal of the acceleration are clearly evident.

2.4 Operator-paced Free-transfer Machine

With all the transfer systems described earlier it is usual for the cycle of operations to occur at a fixed rate and any manual operations involved must keep pace. This is referred to as *machine pacing.* Machines are available, however, where a new cycle of operations can only be initiated when signals are received indicating that all the previous operations have been completed. This is referred to as *operator pacing.*

One basic characteristic which is common to all the systems described is that a breakdown of any individual workhead will stop the whole machine and production will cease until the fault has been cleared. One type of in-line intermittent operator-paced machine, known as a *free-transfer* machine (Fig. 2.15) does not have

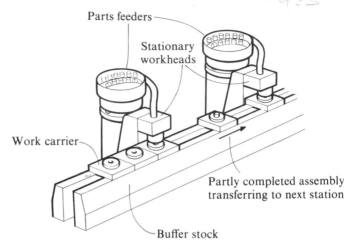

Parts feeders

Stationary
workheads

Work carrier

Partly completed assembly
transferring to next station

Buffer stock

Figure 2.15. In-line free-transfer machine.

this limitation. In this design, the spacing of the workstations is such that *buffer stocks* of assemblies can accumulate between adjacent stations. Each workhead or operator works independently and the assembly process is initiated by the arrival of a work carrier at the station. The first operation is to lift the work carrier clear of the continuously moving chain conveyor and clamp it in position. After the assembly operation has been completed, the work carrier is released and transferred to the next station by the conveyor, provided that a vacant space is available. Thus, on a free-transfer machine a fault at any one station will not necessarily prevent the other stations from working. It will be seen later that this can be an important factor when considering the economics of various transfer machines for mechanized assembly.

Reference

1. HUBY, E. 'Assembly Machine Transfer Systems.' Paper presented at the Conference on Mechanized Assembly, July 1966, Royal College of Advanced Technology, Salford.

3.

Vibratory Bowl Feeders (Miss Chapter)

The vibratory bowl feeder is the most versatile of all hopper feeding devices for small engineering parts. In this feeder (Fig. 3.1) the track along which the parts travel is helical in form and passes round the inside wall of a shallow cylindrical hopper or bowl. The bowl is usually supported on three sets of inclined leaf springs secured to a heavy base. Vibration is applied to the bowl from an electromagnet mounted on the base and the support system constrains the movement of the bowl so that it has an angular vibration about its vertical axis together with a vertical vibration. The motion is such that any part of the inclined track vibrates along a short, approximately straight path, which is inclined to the horizontal at an angle

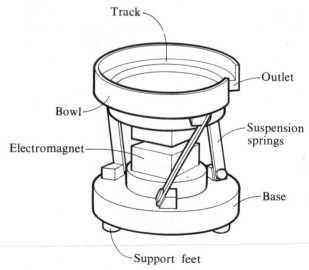

Figure 3.1. Vibratory bowl feeder.

23

greater than that of the track. When component parts are placed in the bowl, the effect of the vibratory motion is to cause them to climb up the track to the outlet at the top of the bowl. Before considering the characteristics of vibratory bowl feeders it is necessary to examine the mechanics of vibratory conveying. For this purpose it is convenient to deal with the motion of a part on a straight vibrating track which is inclined at a small angle to the horizontal.

3.1 Mechanics of Vibratory Conveying

In the following analysis, the track of a vibratory feeder is assumed to move bodily with simple harmonic motion along a straight path inclined at an angle $(\theta + \psi)$ to the horizontal (Fig. 3.2). θ is the angle of inclination of the track and thus ψ is the angle between the track and its line of vibration. The frequency of vibration f (usually 50 cycles per second in practice) is conveniently expressed in analysis as $\omega = 2\pi f$ rad/sec. The amplitude of vibration, a_0, and the instantaneous velocity and acceleration of the track may all be resolved in directions parallel and normal to the track. These components will be referred to as 'parallel' and 'normal' motions and the normal motions will be indicated by the suffix n.

It will be assumed in the analysis that the motion of a part (mass m_p) is independent of its shape and that air resistance is negligible. It will also be assumed that there is no tendency for the part to roll down the track.

It is useful to consider the behaviour of a part which is placed on a track whose amplitude of vibration is increased gradually from zero. For small amplitudes the part will remain stationary on the

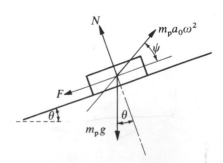

Figure 3.2. Forces acting on a part in vibratory feeding.

track because the parallel inertia force acting on it will be too small to overcome the frictional resistance, F, between the part and the track. Figure 3.2 shows the maximum inertia force acting on the part when the track is at the upper limit of its motion. This force has parallel and normal components of $m_p a_0 \omega^2 \cos \psi$ and $m_p a_0 \omega^2 \sin \psi$ respectively and it can be seen that for sliding up the track to occur:

$$m_p a_0 \omega^2 \cos \psi > m_p g \sin \theta + F \qquad (3.1)$$

where

$$F = \mu_s N = \mu_s (m_p g \cos \theta - m_p a_0 \omega^2 \sin \psi) \qquad (3.2)$$

and where μ_s = coefficient of static friction between part and track. The condition for forward (i.e., up the track) sliding to occur is therefore given by combining eq. (3.1) and (3.2). Thus:

$$\frac{a_0 \omega^2}{g} > \frac{\sin \theta + \mu_s \cos \theta}{\cos \psi + \mu_s \sin \psi} \qquad (3.3)$$

Similarly, it can be shown that for backward sliding to occur during the vibration cycle:

$$\frac{a_0 \omega^2}{g} > \frac{\mu_s \cos \theta - \sin \theta}{\cos \psi - \mu_s \sin \psi} \qquad (3.4)$$

The operating conditions of a vibratory conveyor may be expressed in terms of the dimensionless normal track acceleration A_n/g_n where:

$$A_n = \text{normal track acceleration}$$

$$= a_n \omega^2 = a_0 \omega^2 \sin \psi$$

and

$$g_n = \text{normal acceleration due to gravity} = g \cos \theta$$

Thus:

$$\frac{A_n}{g_n} = \frac{a_0 \omega^2 \sin \psi}{g \cos \theta} \qquad (3.5)$$

Substitution of eq. (3.5) in eqs. (3.3) and (3.4) gives:
  For forward sliding:

$$\frac{A_n}{g_n} > \frac{\tan \theta + \mu_s}{\cot \psi + \mu_s} \qquad (3.6)$$

For backward sliding:

$$\frac{A_n}{g_n} > \frac{\mu_s - \tan \theta}{\cot \psi - \mu_s} \tag{3.7}$$

For values of $\mu_s = 0.8$, $\theta = 3$ degrees and $\psi = 30$ degrees, eqs. (3.6) and (3.7) show that the ratio A_n/g_n must be greater than 0·34 for forward sliding to occur and greater than 0·81 for backward sliding. With these conditions it is clear that, for all amplitudes of vibration giving a value of A_n/g_n greater than 0·34, forward sliding will predominate and the part will climb the track, sliding forward or both forward and backward during each vibration cycle.

The limiting condition for forward conveying to occur is given by equating eqs. (3.6) and (3.7). Thus, for forward conveying:

$$\tan \psi > \frac{\tan \theta}{\mu_s^2}$$

or, when θ is small:

$$\tan \psi > \frac{\theta}{\mu_s^2} \tag{3.8}$$

for values of $\mu_s = 0.8$ and $\theta = 3$ degrees, ψ must be greater than 4·7 degrees for forward conveying to occur.

For sufficiently large vibration amplitudes the part will leave the track and 'hop' forward during each cycle. The condition for this to occur is where the normal reaction, N, between the part and the track becomes zero.

From Fig. 3.2.

$$N = m_p g \cos \theta - m_p a_0 \omega^2 \sin \psi \tag{3.9}$$

and therefore for the part to leave the track

$$\frac{a_0 \omega^2}{g} > \frac{\cos \theta}{\sin \psi}$$

or

$$\frac{A_n}{g_n} > 1.0 \tag{3.10}$$

It is clear from the earlier examples, however, that the part would slide forward before it leaves the track during each cycle.

Fig. 3.3 illustrates graphically the equations derived above. This shows the effect of the vibration angle (ψ) on the limiting values of the dimensionless normal acceleration (A_n/g_n) for forward sliding to occur, for both forward and backward sliding, and for the part to 'hop' along the track.

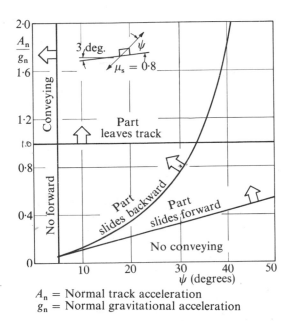

A_n = Normal track acceleration
g_n = Normal gravitational acceleration

Figure 3.3. Limiting conditions for various modes of vibratory conveying.

The detailed types of motion which may occur in vibratory feeding and described in previous literature are conveniently illustrated by the velocity-time diagrams presented in Figs. 3.4 and 3.5. Figure 3.4 shows five possible modes of conveying where the part is conveyed up an inclined track without losing contact (thus for these examples $A_n/g_n < 1\cdot0$). In the figure, the absolute parallel velocities of the track and part are plotted against time. In each case the part starts to slide forward at some point when the track is nearing the upper limit of its motion. This forward sliding continues until the track is nearing the lower limit of its motion, at which point the part may remain stationary relative to the track until the cycle is complete (Fig. 3.4a) or slide backward until the cycle is

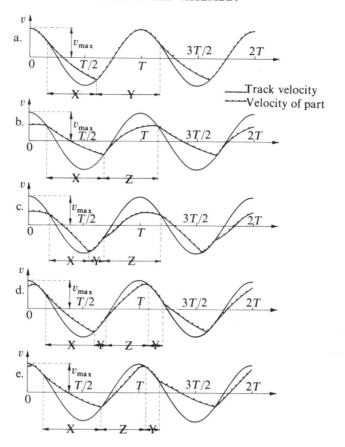

T = Periodic time

v_{max} = Maximum track velocity in the direction of the track

v = Velocity in the direction of the track

X = Region where the part is sliding forward relative to the track

Y = Region where the part is stationary relative to the track

Z = Region where the part is sliding backward relative to the track

Figure 3.4. Various modes of 'sliding' conveying.

complete (Fig. 3.4b). In some cases a stationary period is followed by a period of backward sliding only (Fig. 3.4c) or backward sliding followed by yet another stationary period (Fig. 3.4d). Finally in

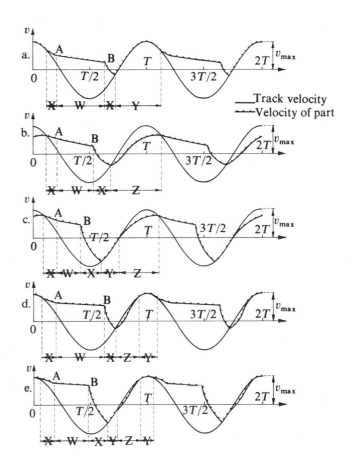

T = Periodic time
v_{max} = Maximum track velocity in the direction
  of the track
v = Velocity in the direction of the track
W = Region where the part is in free flight
X = Region where the part is sliding forward
  relative to the track
Y = Region where the part is stationary relative
  to the track
Z = Region where the part is sliding backward
  relative to the track

Figure 3.5. Various modes of 'hopping' conveying.

Fig. 3.4e the forward sliding is followed by a period of backward sliding and then a stationary period to complete the cycle.

The various possibilities described may be illustrated by a simple flow diagram as follows:

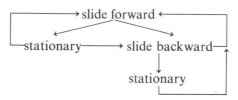

Analysis and experiment have shown that higher feed rates are obtained with the 'hopping' mode of conveying (i.e., when $A_n/g_n > 1.0$). A further five possible modes of conveying are now obtained and these are shown in Fig. 3.5 in the form of velocity–time diagrams and summarized by the flow diagram below:

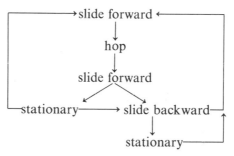

Clearly, a complete analysis of all the possible modes of vibratory conveying is complicated. Such an analysis has been made[1] and leads to equations which must be solved with the aid of a digital computer. For the purposes of the present discussion it is considered adequate to describe only the main results of this analysis and the results of some experimental tests. In the following the effects of frequency, f, track acceleration, A_n/g_n, track angle, θ, vibration angle, ψ, and the effective coefficient of friction, μ, on the mean conveying velocity, v_m, will be dealt with separately.

3.2   Effect of Frequency

One principal result of theoretical work is that for given conditions and for a constant track acceleration (i.e., A_n/g_n is constant) the mean conveying velocity, v_m, is inversely proportional to the vibration frequency, f.

Hence

$$fv_m = \text{constant} \qquad (3.11)$$

This is illustrated in Fig. 3.6 where the effect of track acceleration on the mean conveying velocity is plotted for three values of the vibration angle, ψ. It can be seen that the experimental points for a range of frequencies fall on one line when the factor fv_m is used as a measure of the conveying velocity. This verifies the prediction of the theoretical analysis (eq. (3.11)). One consequence of this result is that for high conveying velocities and hence high feed rates it is desirable to use as low a frequency as practicable. However, since the track accelerations must be kept constant, this means a corresponding increase in track amplitude. Due to the mechanical problems of connecting the feeder to a stationary machine this imposes a lower limit on the frequency. The results of experiments[1] have shown that some advantage is to be gained from lowering the operating frequency of a bowl feeder from the usual 50 cycles per second to 25 cycles per second.

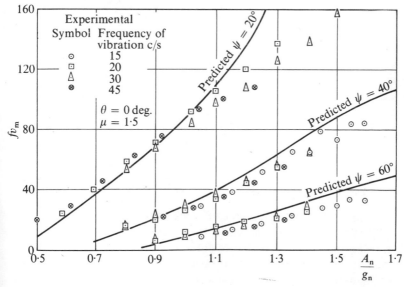

ψ = Vibration angle, degrees; f = Frequency, c/s; θ = Track angle, degrees; μ = Coefficient of friction; v_m = mean conveying velocity, in/sec.

Figure 3.6. Effect of vibration angle, track acceleration, and frequency on conveying velocity. (After Redford[1].)

3.3 Effect of Track Acceleration

Figure 3.6 shows that an increase in track acceleration A_n/g_n generally produces an increase in conveying velocity. At some point, however, although the theoretical analysis predicts further increases in velocity, increases in A_n/g_n cease to have a significant effect. This may be explained as follows:

As the track acceleration is increased until $A_n/g_n > 1.0$ the part starts to hop once during each cycle as described earlier. At first, the velocity of impact as the part lands on the track is small but, as the track acceleration is increased further, the impact velocity also increases until, at some critical value, the part starts to bounce. Under these circumstances the feeding cycle becomes erratic and unstable and the theoretical predictions are no longer valid.

To obtain the most efficient feeding conditions it is necessary to operate with values of A_n/g_n greater than unity but below the values which will produce unstable conditions. From Fig. 3.6 it can be seen that within this range an approximately linear relationship exists between the factors fv_m and A_n/g_n for each value of ψ and for given values of track angle, θ, and coefficient of friction, μ.

3.4 Effect of Vibration Angle

From Fig. 3.6 it can be seen that the conveying velocity is sensitive to changes in the vibration angle, ψ. The effect is shown more clearly in Fig. 3.7, which indicates that an optimum vibration angle exists for given conditions. For clarity, these theoretical predictions are shown without the supporting experimental evidence. Previous work[1] has resulted in the relationship between optimum vibration angle, ψ_{opt}, and coefficient of friction shown in Fig. 3.8 for a practical value of track acceleration, $A_n/g_n = 1.2$.

3.5 Effect of Track Angle

Figure 3.9 shows the effect of track angle, θ, on the conveying velocity for various track accelerations when $\mu = 0.2$. These results show that the highest velocities are always achieved when the track angle is zero and secondly that forward conveying is only obtained with small track angles. The mechanical design of a bowl feeder necessitates a positive track angle of three or four degrees in order to raise the parts to the bowl outlet. However, it can be seen from the figure that even if conveying can be achieved on the track, the mean conveying velocity will be significantly lower than that around

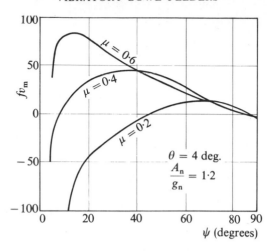

Figure 3.7. Theoretical results showing effect of vibration angle on mean conveying velocity. (After Redford[1].)

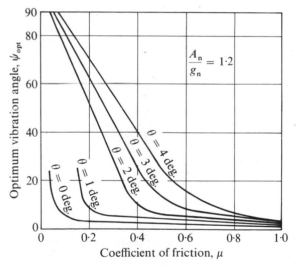

Figure 3.8. Theoretical results showing effect of coefficient of friction on the optimum vibration angle. (After Redford[1].)

the flat bowl base. This means that in practice the parts on the track will invariably be pushed along by those in the bottom of the bowl which will be circulating at a greater speed. This leads to certain problems in the design of the orienting devices, which are generally

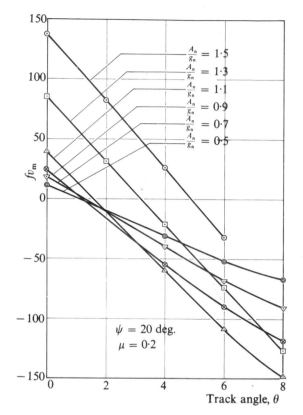

Figure 3.9. Theoretical results showing effect of track angle on conveying velocity. (After Redford[1].)

placed around the upper part of the bowl track. During the testing of such orienting devices, parts transported individually along the track may behave correctly. However, when the bowl is filled with parts and a queue forms along the track, the parts tend to be forced through the orienting devices by the pressure of those in the bottom of the bowl. This may often lead to jamming and general unreliability in operation.

From the above discussion it is also clear that when considering the unrestricted feed rate from a bowl feeder, a track angle of zero degrees should be employed because the feeding characteristics in the flat bowl bottom will generally govern the overall performance of the feeder.

3.6 Effect of Coefficient of Friction

The practical range of coefficient of friction in vibratory feeding is from 0·2 to 1·0. The figure of 0·2 is representative of a steel part conveyed on a steel track. By lining the track with rubber, a common practice in industry, the coefficient of friction may be raised to approximately 0·8.

Figure 3.10 shows the effect of the coefficient of friction on the conveying velocity for a horizontal track, a vibration angle of 20 degrees and for various track accelerations. It can be seen that for practical values of track acceleration, an increase in μ leads to an increase in conveying velocity, hence the advantage of increasing friction by lining the tracks of bowl feeders with rubber.

3.7 Load Sensitivity

One of the main disadvantages of vibratory bowl feeders is their change in performance as the bowl gradually empties. This is

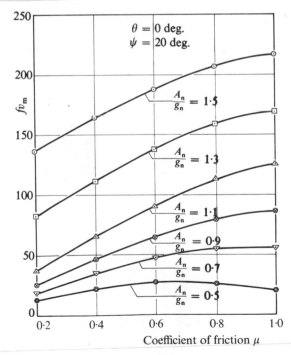

Figure 3.10. Theoretical results showing effect of coefficient of friction on conveying velocity. (After Redford[1].)

because, for a constant power input the amplitude of vibration, and hence the maximum bowl acceleration, usually increases as the effective mass of the loaded bowl reduces. It can be deduced from Fig. 3.6 that this increase in bowl acceleration will generally result in an increase in the unrestricted feed rate. Vibratory bowl feeders are often used to convey and orient parts for mechanized assembly and, since the workheads on an assembly machine are designed to work at a fixed cycle time, the parts can only leave the feeder at a uniform rate. The feeder must therefore be adjusted to overfeed slightly under all conditions of loading, and excess parts are continuously returned from the track to the bottom of the bowl.

The change in performance as a feeder gradually empties is referred to as its load sensitivity and the upper curve in Fig. 3.11 shows how the unrestricted feed rate for a commercial bowl feeder

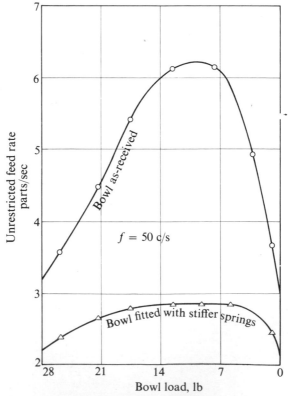

Figure 3.11. *Experimentally determined load sensitivity of a commercial vibratory bowl feeder feeding $\frac{5}{16}$ in. dia × 1 in. long steel parts.*

(in the as-received condition) varied as the bowl emptied. It can be seen that the maximum feed rate occurred when the bowl was approximately 25 per cent full and that this represented an increase of approximately 100 per cent on the feed rate obtained with the bowl full. It is of interest to compare this result with the measured changes in bowl acceleration shown in Fig. 3.12 where it can be

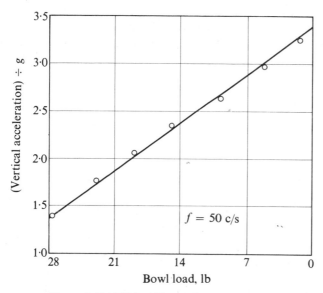

Figure 3.12. Effect of bowl load on bowl acceleration.

seen that the bowl acceleration, and hence the amplitude, increased continuously until the bowl became empty. Clearly, when a feeder empties the feed rate will reduce to zero, but Fig. 3.11 shows that the feed rate began to reduce much sooner than might be expected from Fig. 3.12. This behaviour is considered to be due to the greater velocity of parts in the flat bowl bottom than that on the track. This was described earlier and when the bowl is full the feed rate depends mainly on the feeding characteristics in the bottom of the bowl where the general circulation of parts pushes those on the track. However, when the bowl empties sufficiently so that its contents are mainly held on the track, the pushing action ceases and the feed rate depends on the conveying velocity on the inclined track which is generally lower than that on a horizontal surface.

This explains the difference in character between the graphs in Figs. 3.11 and 3.12.

Figure 3.11 suggests that under the test conditions the as-received bowl feeder could be used to feed a workhead operating at a maximum rate of three cycles per second and that in this case there would be considerable recirculation of parts due to overfeeding. Assuming that the feeder were to be refilled when it became 25 per cent full then the feeding characteristics between refills may be reasonably represented by a feed rate increasing linearly as the bowl empties. An analysis is now presented which may be used to estimate the unnecessary recirculation of parts in a bowl feeder with this characteristic.

3.8   Effect of Load Sensitivity on Recirculation of Parts

For the purposes of the following analysis, the load sensitivity of a bowl feeder, S per cent, will be defined as the percentage change in unrestricted feed rate between refills. It will be assumed that between refills the unrestricted feed rate increases linearly with reductions in bowl loading.

In the analysis it is necessary to consider the motion of parts during incremental changes in bowl load when the feeder is connected to a machine which uses parts at a constant rate. During any load increment, $F_m t_1$ parts will leave the bowl, where t_1 is the time taken for a load increment and F_m is the machine rate (parts/sec).

For the first load increment, the average unrestricted feed rate F_1 will be given by:

$$F_1 = F_m \left(1 + \frac{S}{100 m_t} - \frac{S}{200 m_t} \right) \qquad (3.12)$$

where m_t is the total number of load increments between refills. Generally, for the nth increment in load the average unrestricted feed rate F_n will be given by:

$$F_n = F_m \left(1 + \frac{Sn}{100 m_t} - \frac{S}{200 m_t} \right) \qquad (3.13)$$

The number of parts, N_n, presented to the bowl outlet during the nth increment in load will be given by:

$$N_n = F_n t_1 = F_m t_1 \left(1 + \frac{Sn}{100 m_t} - \frac{S}{200 m_t} \right) \qquad (3.14)$$

For any increment, only $F_m t_1$ parts actually leave the bowl and therefore the number returned to the bottom of the bowl, R_n (recirculation during nth increment), is given by:

$$R_n = N_n - F_m t_1 = F_m t_1 S \left(\frac{2n - 1}{200 m_t} \right) \tag{3.15}$$

If L_p is the total number of parts placed in the bowl at each refill, then during any load increment L_p/m_t parts will leave the bowl and thus:

$$L_p/m_t = F_m t_1 \tag{3.16}$$

and generally the average bowl load, L_n, during the nth increment of load, will be given by:

$$L_n = L_p \left(1 - \frac{n}{m_t} + \frac{1}{2m_t} \right) \tag{3.17}$$

neglecting the parts present in the bowl immediately before a refill. During the nth increment of load each part will recirculate on average R_n/L_n times and thus the average recirculation per part will be given, from eqs. (3.15) and (3.17), by:

$$\frac{R_n}{L_n} = \frac{S}{100 m_t} \left(\frac{2n - 1}{2m_t - 2n + 1} \right) \tag{3.18}$$

The total average recirculation, R_T, for any load increment will now be given by the recirculation for that increment plus the sum of the recirculations for the preceding increments. Thus:

$$R_T = \frac{S}{100 m_t} \sum_{n=1}^{n=n} \left(\frac{2n - 1}{2m_t - 2n + 1} \right) \tag{3.19}$$

Figure 3.13 now shows how the average total recirculation of parts in a bowl varies with bowl load for various values of the load sensitivity, S; the curves being computed using eq. (3.19).

The analysis has assumed that all the parts arrive at the bowl outlet correctly oriented and Fig. 3.13 shows that in this case, with 100 per cent load sensitivity, the last few parts fed before a refill will have been recirculated four times on average. This recirculation of parts is clearly inefficient and may cause excessive wear and damage. It is therefore important to consider means whereby the load sensitivity of bowl feeders may be reduced.

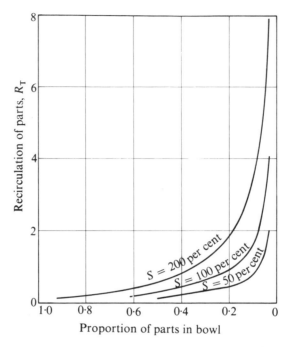

Figure 3.13. *Effect of load sensitivity, S, on average recirculation of parts due to overfeeding.*

3.9 Reduction of Load Sensitivity

Frequency response curves for the vibratory bowl feeder used in the above experiments are presented in Fig. 3.14. These curves show the effect of changes in the forcing frequency on the bowl acceleration for a constant power input and for various bowl loadings. In these tests the power input was less than that employed for the results in Fig. 3.12 but they show the same effect. For a forcing frequency of 50 c/s, the maximum bowl acceleration was sensitive to changes in bowl loading. However, it can also be seen that for a forcing frequency of approximately 44 c/s, the bowl acceleration was approximately constant for all bowl loadings. Under these conditions the load sensitivity would be considerably reduced. Alternatively, if the spring stiffness of the bowl supports were to be increased sufficiently it is clear that this would have the effect of shifting the response curves so that the changes in bowl acceleration would be minimized for a forcing frequency of 50 c/s. The natural

frequency of the empty as-received bowl was approximately 53 c/s
and tests showed that if this was increased to 61 c/s by increasing
the support spring stiffness, the load sensitivity of the feeder was
considerably reduced. The lower curve in Fig. 3.11 shows this effect.
It can also be seen, however, that the feed rates have been reduced
by stiffening the support springs and therefore, in order to maintain
the higher feed rate, a more powerful drive would be required.

3.10   Orientation of Parts

One of the main reasons for the wide application of the vibratory
bowl feeder is its ability to feed and orient a large majority of the
small parts used in engineering assembly work. The various methods
of orienting parts will be dealt with in chapter 5.

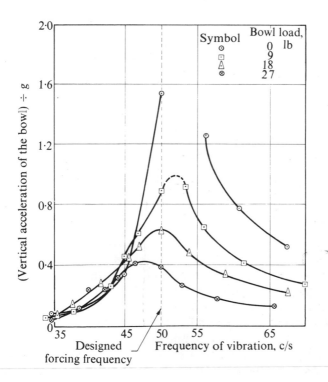

*Figure 3.14. Frequency response curves for a vibratory bowl feeder showing
effect of bowl load. (After Redford[1].)*

3.11 Bowl Feeder Design

The following gives a summary of the results and conclusions obtained in the work described above, which would be useful in the design of a vibratory bowl feeder:

(a) For a given track acceleration, the mean conveying velocity in a vibratory bowl feeder is inversely proportional to the operating frequency;

(b) For a given frequency, an increase in vibration amplitude (or track acceleration) will increase the conveying velocity. However, with large accelerations the behaviour of the parts becomes erratic and unpredictable;

(c) For maximum conveying velocity the track angle should be as small as possible. However, feeding around the flat bowl bottom will always be faster than on the inclined track and therefore the parts will generally be pushed up the track by the circulation of those in the bowl;

(d) An optimum vibration angle exists for any given conditions;

(e) Higher coefficients of friction between the parts and the track will generally give higher conveying velocities;

(f) For any bowl feeder a support spring stiffness may be chosen which will give a reasonably low load sensitivity. However, with many commercial feeders this will necessitate an increase in the power available from the electromagnet in order to maintain a sufficiently high feed rate.

3.12 Spiral Elevators

A device commonly employed for elevating and feeding component parts is the spiral elevator. A typical spiral elevator is illustrated in Fig. 3.15 and it can be seen that the drive is identical to that used for a vibratory bowl feeder. The helical track up which the parts are conveyed passes round the outside of a cylindrical tube. This device is not generally used to orient parts because they cannot readily be rejected back into the hopper bowl situated at the base of the elevator. Since the mode of conveying of the parts is identical to that obtained with a vibratory bowl feeder, the results and discussion presented above and the design recommendations made will apply equally to the spiral elevator.

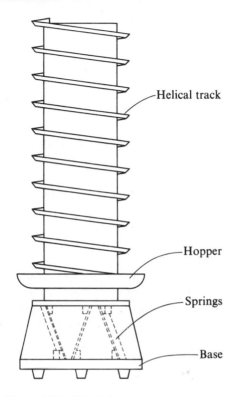

Figure 3.15. Spiral elevator.

Reference

1. REDFORD, A. H. 'Vibratory Conveyors.' Ph.D. Thesis, Royal College of Advanced Technology, Salford, 1966.

4.

Some Other Parts Feeding Devices

Although the vibratory bowl feeder is the most widely employed and most versatile parts feeding device, many other types of parts feeder are available. Usually these are only suitable for feeding certain basic types of component part generally classifiable by their shapes but when feeding these parts better results may be obtained for a smaller capital outlay with feeders other than the vibratory type.

One point which must be borne in mind when considering parts feeders is that, in mechanized assembly, the output of parts from the feeder is always restricted by the machine being fed. The machine will generally use parts at a strictly uniform rate and this may be referred to as the *machine rate.* In the design and testing of parts feeders it is often convenient to observe the feed rate when the feeder is not connected to a machine, i.e., when no restriction is applied to the output of the feeder. The feed rate under these circumstances will be referred to as the *unrestricted feed rate.* Clearly, in practice the mean unrestricted feed rate must not fall below the machine rate.

Certain other general requirements of parts feeders may be summarized as follows:

The unrestricted feed rate should not vary widely since this will simply mean that when the feeder is connected to a machine, the parts will be continuously re-circulated within the feeder for much of the time. This will cause excessive wear and may eventually damage the parts. This undesirable characteristic often occurs in parts feeders where the feed rate is sensitive to changes in the quantity of parts present in the feeder and will be referred to as the load sensitivity of the feeder.

With parts feeders suitable for automatic machines it is necessary that all the parts be presented to the machine in the same attitude, i.e., they must be fed correctly oriented. Some feeders are able to feed and orient many types of part whilst others are only able to handle a very limited range of part shapes.

Undoubtedly the reliability of a parts feeder is one of its most important characteristics. Parts feeders should be designed so that the possibility of parts jamming in the feeder, or in its orienting devices, is minimized or eliminated.

It is sometimes suggested that parts feeders can also act as inspection devices. It is possible to design certain parts feeders so that mis-shapen parts, swarf, etc. will not be fed to the machine but will be rejected by the device fitted to the feeder. This can be an important feature because defective parts or foreign matter, if fed to the machine, will probably cause a breakdown and may stop the whole production line.

Some parts feeders are noisy in operation and some tend to damage certain types of part. Obviously both these aspects of parts feeding must be considered when studying the possible alternatives for a particular application.

Parts feeders can generally be classified into: reciprocating feeders; rotary feeders; belt feeders; and finally vibratory feeders which have been dealt with in the previous chapter. A selection of the more common feeding devices within each of the above groups will now be described and discussed.

4.1 Reciprocating Tube Hopper

A reciprocating tube hopper is illustrated in Fig. 4.1 and consists of a conical hopper with a hole in the centre through which a delivery tube passes. Relative vertical motion between the hopper and the tube is achieved by reciprocating either the tube or the hopper. During the period when the top of the tube is below the level of parts, some parts will fall into the delivery tube. It is usual to machine the top of the tube at an angle so that a part resting across the opening will fall clear and not block the opening as the tube is pushed upward through the mass of parts. Care must be taken in choosing the angle of the conical hopper because if the angle is too small there is a possibility of parts jamming between the tube and the hopper.

Figure 4.2 shows the forces acting on a cylindrical part jammed in this way when the tube is moving downward relative to the hopper.

The force W_p acting vertically downward represents the weight of the part together with any additional force which may be present due to parts resting on top of the one shown.

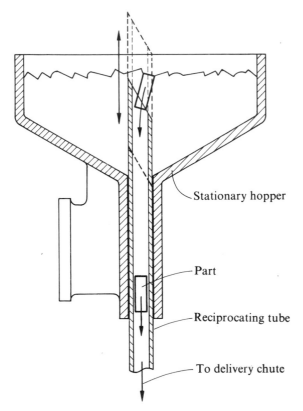

Figure 4.1. Reciprocating tube hopper.

Resolving forces vertically and horizontally and taking moments about A gives:

$$F_1 + W_p + F_2 \cos \phi = N_2 \sin \phi \tag{4.1}$$

$$N_1 = N_2 \cos \phi + F_2 \sin \phi \tag{4.2}$$

$$F_1(1 + \cos \phi)\left(\frac{d}{2}\right) + W_p\left(\frac{d}{2}\right)\cos \phi = N_1\left(\frac{d}{2}\right)\sin \phi \tag{4.3}$$

where ϕ is the hopper wall angle and d is the diameter of the part.
Eliminating W_p from eqs. (4.1) and (4.3) gives, after rearrangement:

$$N_1 \sin \phi = F_1(1 + \cos \phi) + \cos \phi(N_2 \sin \phi - F_2 \cos \phi - F_1) \tag{4.4}$$

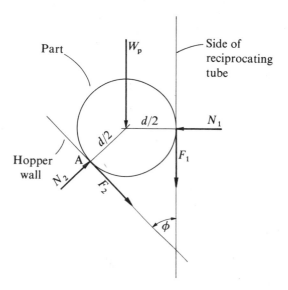

Figure 4.2. Forces acting on part jammed between hopper wall and tube.

The maximum value of F_2 is given by $\mu_s N_2$ (where μ_s is the static coefficient of friction) and thus writing $F_2 = \mu_s N_2$ in eqs. (4.2) and (4.4) and eliminating N_2 gives:

$$\frac{F_1}{N_1} = \frac{\mu_s}{\cos \phi + \mu_s \sin \phi} \tag{4.5}$$

For the tube to slide, $F_1/N_1 > \mu_s$, and therefore from eq. (4.5)

$$\frac{1}{\cos \phi + \mu_s \sin \phi} > 1 \tag{4.6}$$

Equation (4.6) indicates that the value of ϕ should be as large as possible to prevent jamming when μ_s is large. However, when $\mu_s < \cot \phi$ the parts cannot slide down the hopper wall. The best compromise is probably given by writing the limiting conditions:

$$\mu_s = \cot \phi \tag{4.7}$$

and

$$\cos \phi + \mu_s \sin \phi = 1 \tag{4.8}$$

Combining eqs. (4.7) and (4.8) gives $\phi = 60$ degrees and on sub-stituting this value in expression (4.6) we find that, to prevent jamming under these conditions, the coefficient of friction μ_s must be less than 0·577. Since this value is greater than that expected in practice it may be concluded that with a hopper angle of 60 degrees the possibility of jamming will generally be avoided.

4.1.1 *Load Sensitivity*

As the hopper empties the opportunity for the tube to collect parts during each cycle is reduced and hence the mean feed rate also reduces.

4.2 Centreboard Hopper

Figure 4.3 shows a typical centreboard hopper feeder. Basically, this consists of a hopper in which the parts are placed at random and a blade with a shaped track along its upper edge which is periodically pushed upward through the mass of parts. The blade will thus catch a few parts on its track during each cycle and when

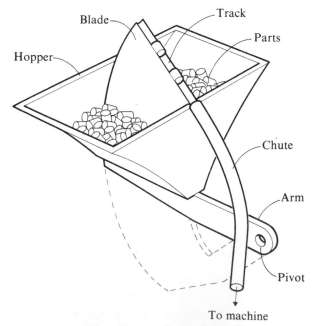

Figure 4.3a. Centreboard hopper.

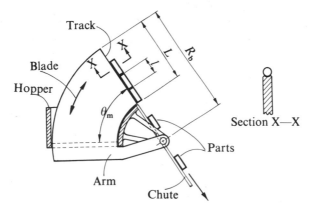

Figure 4.3b. Centreboard hopper.

the blade is in its highest position (as shown in the figure) it is aligned with a chute and the parts will slide down the track and into the chute. The centreboard hopper illustrated is suitable for feeding cylindrical parts.

4.2.1 Feed Rate

One of the important parameters in a centreboard hopper is the angle of inclination of the track when the blade is in its highest position (θ_m in Fig. 4.3b). It will be assumed for the purposes of the following analysis that the cam drive is arranged so that the blade is lifted rapidly to its highest position, allowed to dwell for a period whilst the parts slide into the chute, and is then rapidly returned to its lowest position when the track will be horizontal and aligned with the bottom of the hopper.

Clearly, there will be a limit on the deceleration of the blade on its upward stroke, otherwise the parts will leave the track and be thrown clear of the feeder. Thus, for a given deceleration an increase in the angle θ_m will increase the time taken for the blade to complete its upward motion. However, with larger values of θ_m the time taken for the parts to slide off the track will be less and in choosing θ_m to give maximum frequency of reciprocation and hence maximum feed rate, a compromise must be sought.

The tendency for a part to leave the track during the upward motion of the blade will be greatest at the end of the track farthest away from the pivot. The forces acting on a part in this position are

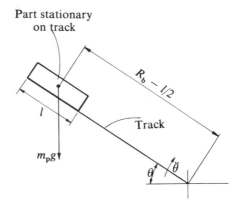

Figure 4.4. *Forces acting on part during upward motion of blade.*

shown in Fig. 4.4 and, from the figure, the condition for the reaction between the part and the track to become zero is given by:

$$m_p \ddot{\theta}(R_b - l/2) = -m_p g \cos \theta_m \tag{4.9}$$

where

m_p = mass of part
R_b = radius from pivot to upper end of track
θ_m = maximum angle between track and horizontal
$\ddot{\theta}$ = angular acceleration of track.

Thus, the maximum angular deceleration of the blade is given by:

$$-\ddot{\theta} = (g \cos \theta_m)/R_b \quad \text{approximately} \tag{4.10}$$

(if l is small compared with R_b).

For simplicity, it will now be assumed that the drive to the blade is designed to give, during the period of the upward motion of the blade, (a) a constant acceleration of $(g \cos \theta_m)/R_b$ followed by (b) a constant deceleration of $(g \cos \theta_m)/R_b$. Under these conditions, the total time T_1 taken to lift the blade so that the track is inclined at an angle θ_m to the horizontal is given by:

$$T_1^2 = 4R_b\theta_m/g \cos \theta_m \tag{4.11}$$

It is now assumed that when the blade is in its highest position, it will dwell for a period T_2 just sufficient to allow the parts to slide down the track. This will be given, in the worst case, by the time taken for one part to slide the whole length of the track. The forces acting on a part under these circumstances are shown in Fig. 4.5 and resolving in a direction parallel to the track gives:

$$m_p a = m_p g \sin \theta_m - \mu_d m_p g \cos \theta_m \qquad (4.12)$$

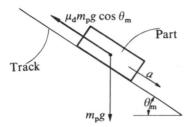

Figure 4.5. Forces acting on part as it slides down track.

where a is the linear acceleration of the part down the track and μ_d is the coefficient of dynamic friction between the part and the track. The minimum dwell period T_2 is now given by:

$$T_2^2 = \frac{2L}{g(\sin \theta_m - \mu_d \cos \theta_m)} \qquad (4.13)$$

where L is the total length of the track.

If the time taken to return the blade to its lowest position is now neglected (since no basic restrictions apply to the accelerations of the blade during this period) then the total period, T_f, of the feeder cycle will be given by:

$$T_f = T_1 + T_2 = \left(\frac{4R_b \theta_m}{g \cos \theta_m} \right)^{\frac{1}{2}} + \left(\frac{2L}{g(\sin \theta_m - \mu_d \cos \theta_m)} \right)^{\frac{1}{2}} \qquad (4.14)$$

Equation (4.14) consists of two terms; one which will increase as θ_m is increased and one which will decrease as θ_m is increased. An optimum value of θ_m always exists which will give minimum period T_f and hence maximum theoretical feed rate. It can be shown mathematically that this optimum value of θ_m is a function only of μ_d and the ratio R_b/L. However, the resulting expression is unmanageable and it has been found that the equation:

$$\theta_{opt} = 27 + 0.7 \tan^{-1} \mu_d \text{ degrees} \qquad (4.15)$$

gives an acceptable approximation to the true solution for a practical value of $R_b/L = 2\cdot0$. Thus, for example, with a coefficient of dynamic friction of $0\cdot5$ the optimum track angle would be approximately 46 degrees.

Figure 4.6 shows how the maximum frequency of the blade cycle f_b (given by $1/T_f$) varies as the coefficient of friction between part and track is changed and when the ratio $R_b/L = 2\cdot0$. It can be seen that for large values of μ_d in the range $0\cdot4$ to $0\cdot8$ the maximum blade frequency only varies by about 10 or 15 per cent. The maximum blade frequency is more sensitive to changes in the length, L, of the track and for longer tracks the frequency is lower. However, it should be remembered that for a given size of part a longer track will on average pick up a greater number of parts per cycle and hence the mean feed rate may increase.

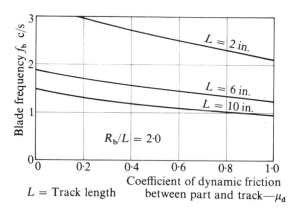

Figure 4.6. Effect of track length and coefficient of friction on maximum blade frequency for a centreboard hopper.

The maximum number of parts which may be selected during each cycle is given by L/l. In practice the average number selected will be less than this and if η is taken to be the 'efficiency' of a particular design then the average number of parts fed during each cycle will be given by $\eta L/l$ and the mean feed rate, F_0, of the hopper feeder will be given by:

$$F_0 = f_b \eta \frac{L}{l} \quad \text{parts/sec} \tag{4.16}$$

where

$$f_b = \frac{1}{T_f} = \text{blade frequency.}$$

It has been seen above that f_b is mainly dependent on the length of the track, L. If a value of $\mu_d = 0.5$ together with the corresponding optimum track angle, $\theta_{opt} = 46$ degrees, is now substituted in eq. (4.14) then

$$T_f = L^{\frac{1}{2}}/3.67$$

or

$$f_b = 3.67/L^{\frac{1}{2}} \tag{4.17}$$

Substitution of eq. (4.17) in eq. (4.16) now gives:

$$F_0 = \frac{3.67}{l}\eta L^{\frac{1}{2}} \quad \text{parts/sec} \tag{4.18}$$

With typical values of $l = 1$ in. and $\eta = 0.2$, Fig. 4.7 shows how the feed rate, F_0, obtained from eq. (4.18) varies with changes in the track length, L. Clearly, for any given design, a longer track length will always produce a higher feed rate.

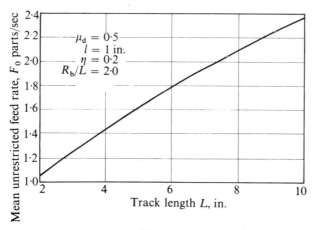

Figure 4.7. *Effect of track length on mean unrestricted feed rate for a centre-board hopper.*

The analysis presented above has considered the theoretical maximum unrestricted feed rate from a centreboard hopper feeder. In practice, because of limitations in the mechanical drive of such a device, the actual feed rate will generally be considerably less than that predicted by the analysis. However, the work indicates that certain trends might be expected from a feeder of this type and these are summarized below;

    (a) The unrestricted feed rate is inversely proportional to the length of the parts for a given design;

    (b) For various designs the unrestricted feed rate is proportional to the square root of the track length when feeding given parts;

    (c) If a high feed rate is required an optimum track angle θ_{opt} exists (the angle of the track when the blade is in its highest position) and this is given approximately by eq. (4.15).

4.2.2 Load Sensitivity and Efficiency

For a centreboard hopper feeder working at a constant frequency, any variation in feed rate as the hopper gradually empties will be due to changes in the efficiency, η. This has been defined as the ratio between the average number of parts selected during one cycle and the maximum number which can be selected. Figures 4.8 and 4.9 show the results of tests on an experimental feeder where $L/l = 6$, $R_b/L = 2$ and $\theta_m = 54$ degrees. The lower curve in Fig. 4.8 shows how the efficiency, η, varied as the hopper gradually emptied and it is interesting to note that a rapid increase in η occurs when less than 100 parts remain in the hopper. The upper curve in Fig. 4.8 shows that this high efficiency can be maintained for all hopper loadings if a baffle is placed on one side of the hopper blade. The baffle would therefore appear to affect the orientation of those parts likely to be selected by the blade. Clearly the load sensitivity characteristics obtained with this latter design approach very closely to the ideal situation. Each of the experimental points in Fig. 4.8 represents the average of eighty results. In Fig. 4.9 one set of eighty results (for a hopper load of 200 parts) is plotted in the form of a frequency curve and exhibits the familiar 'normal' distribution. The average reading in this case was 3·2 and since the maximum number of parts which could be selected by the blade was 6, this represents an efficiency of 53 per cent.

A final design consideration is the inclination of the sloping sides of the hopper. If the inclination is too great there is a possibility that parts will jam between the hopper wall and the blade when the blade is moving downward. This situation is identical to that of the reciprocating tube hopper and the analysis indicated that the included angle between the hopper wall and the blade should be 60 degrees.

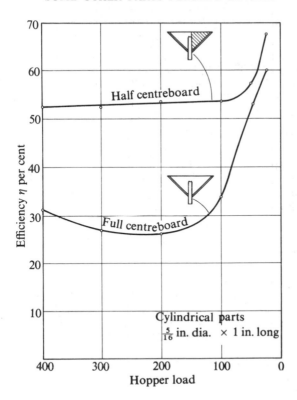

Figure 4.8. Load sensitivity of centreboard hopper.

4.3 Reciprocating Fork Hopper

A reciprocating fork hopper is shown in Fig. 4.10, and is only suitable for feeding headed parts. It consists of a shallow cylindrical bowl which rotates about an axis inclined at approximately 10 degrees to the vertical and a fork which reciprocates in the vertical plane about point A. In its lowest position, the fork is horizontal and rotation of the bowl causes parts to be caught in the fork. The fork then lifts a few parts by their heads to a height sufficient to cause the parts to slide off the fork and into the delivery chute. The analysis for the maximum fork inclination and the maximum rate of reciprocation would be similar to that presented above for a centreboard hopper.

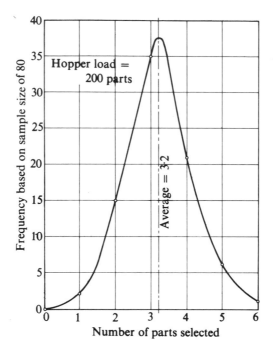

Figure 4.9. Characteristics of centreboard hopper.

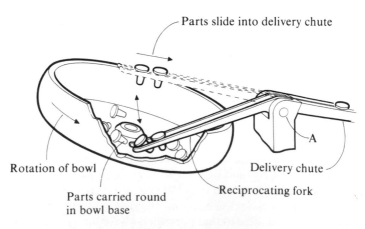

Figure 4.10. Reciprocating fork hopper.

4.3.1 *Load Sensitivity*

As the bowl empties, the possibility of a part engaging with the fork reduces. The feed rate of the feeder will therefore fall as the bowl load decreases.

4.4 External Gate Hopper

An external gate hopper basically consists (Fig. 4.11) of a rotating cylinder having slots in its wall where the cylindrical parts, if oriented correctly, can nest against the wall of the stationary outer sleeve. At some point, as the cylinder rotates, the slots pass over a gate in the outer sleeve which allows the parts to drop one-by-one into the delivery chute. The tumbling action caused by rotation of the cylinder provides repeated opportunities for parts to fall into the slots and subsequently to pass through the external gate into the chute.

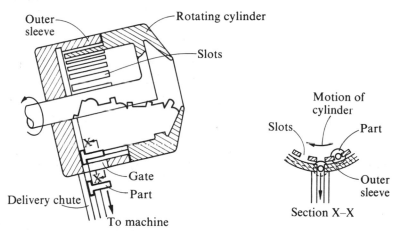

Figure 4.11. External gate hopper (suitable for feeding rivets). (After (1).)

4.4.1 *Feed Rate*

Figure 4.12a shows an enlarged cross-section of the slot and part just before the part falls through the gate. In the following analysis an equation is developed for the maximum peripheral velocity of the inner cylinder for feeding to occur. Clearly if the velocity is too high the part will pass over the gate. At some limiting velocity v the part will neither fall through the gate nor pass over but will become jammed between the corners B and C of the slot and gate as shown in Fig. 4.12b. With any velocity below v the part will drop through the

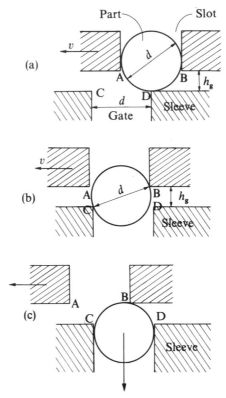

Figure 4.12. Various stages in motion of part when passing through the gate of an external gate hopper.

gate as shown in Fig. 4.12c. The position shown in Fig. 4.12a represents the point at which the part starts to fall. In Fig. 4.12b the part has moved from this position a horizontal distance

$$(d - 0.5(d^2 - h_g^2)^{\frac{1}{2}})$$

which, at a velocity v represents a time interval of

$$(d - 0.5(d^2 - h_g^2)^{\frac{1}{2}})/v.$$

During this time the part has fallen a distance $(d/2 - h_g/2)$ and if it is assumed that the part has fallen freely then the time taken will be given by $[2(d/2 - h_g/2)/g]^{\frac{1}{2}}$. Thus by equating these times, the limiting velocity will be given by:

$$(d - 0.5(d^2 - h_g^2)^{\frac{1}{2}})/v = [(d - h_g)/g]^{\frac{1}{2}} \qquad (4.19)$$

To give the largest values of v, the gap, h_g, between the cylinder and sleeve should be as large as possible. For values of h_g greater than $d/2$ there will be a danger of the parts becoming jammed between the corner B of the slot and the inner surface of the sleeve. Thus, taking $h_g = d/2$ eq. (4.19) becomes, after rearrangement:

$$v = 15 \cdot 8 d^{\frac{1}{2}} \text{ in/sec} \qquad (4.20)$$

If a_s is now taken to be the distance between adjacent slots of the cylinder, then the maximum feed rate, F_{max}, from the feeder will be:

$$F_{max} = v/a_s = 15 \cdot 8 d^{\frac{1}{2}}/a_s \text{ parts/sec} \qquad (4.21)$$

In general, only a proportion of the slots will catch parts and if η is taken to be the 'efficiency' of the feeder then the actual feed rate will be given by:

$$F_0 = 15 \cdot 8 \eta d^{\frac{1}{2}}/a_s \text{ parts/sec} \qquad (4.22)$$

The type of feeder analysed above is generally used for feeding rivets where the slots in the inner cylinder are 'open ended' to allow for the rivet heads. If the diameter of the rivet head is D_h then the minimum theoretical distance between the centres of the slots is given by $a_s - D_h$ and eq. (4.22) becomes:

$$F_0 = 15 \cdot 8 \eta (d/D_h)/d^{\frac{1}{2}} \text{ parts/sec} \qquad (4.23)$$

and for plain cylindrical parts:

$$F_0 = 15 \cdot 8 \eta/d^{\frac{1}{2}} \text{ parts/sec} \qquad (4.24)$$

Taking, as an example, the feeding of rivets with a ratio of head diameter to shank diameter of $D_h/d = 2 \cdot 0$ and an efficiency for the feeder of $0 \cdot 1$, then the relation between feed rate and rivet diameter would be:

$$F_0 = \frac{0 \cdot 1 \times 15 \cdot 8}{2 d^{\frac{1}{2}}} = 0 \cdot 79/d^{\frac{1}{2}} \text{ parts/sec}$$

This relation between feed rate and rivet diameter is shown graphically in Fig. 4.13.

This analysis has considered the maximum possible feed rate from an external gate feeder. In practical designs the actual feed rate will be less than this because of mechanical limitations but the result

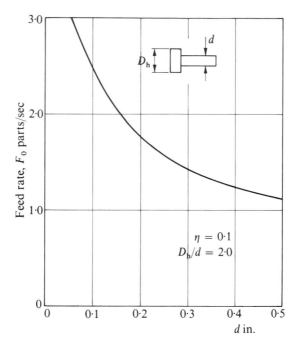

Figure 4.13. *Effect of rivet diameter on feed rate from external gate hopper.*

indicates that certain trends might be expected from this type of feeder and these are now summarized:

(a) The maximum unrestricted feed rate is inversely proportional to the square root of the diameter of a cylindrical part;

(b) When feeding rivets the maximum feed rate is proportional to the ratio of shank diameter to head diameter and inversely proportional to the square root of the shank diameter;

(c) If a high feed rate is required then the slots in the inner cylinder of the feeder should be as close as possible.

4.4.2 Load Sensitivity and Efficiency

The unrestricted feed rate for a given design of feeder depends on η, the efficiency. This may be affected by the load in the hopper, the angle of inclination of the feeder axis and the position of the external gate. Tests have shown that the most significant of these variables is the angle of inclination, λ, of the feeder axis. The results presented in Fig. 4.14 indicate that λ should be as low as possible for maximum efficiency.

However, it should be realized that a practical limitation exists because, as λ is reduced, the capacity of the hopper is also reduced and a compromise must therefore be reached in any given design. The results in Fig. 4.14 also show that the efficiency of the feeder increases rapidly as the hopper empties. Figure 4.15 shows the effect of the angular position, ϕ_g, of the external gate on the efficiency. It is clear that for values of ϕ_g greater than 90 degrees, the efficiency

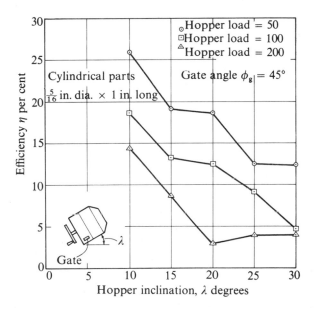

Figure 4.14. Effect of hopper inclination on efficiency of external gate hopper.

would become zero and for very small values of ϕ_g the chances of parts falling into the slots is reduced. The results show that an optimum exists when ϕ_g is approximately 45 degrees and Fig. 4.14 shows that, with this optimum value and with the lowest practical value of $\lambda = 10$ degrees, the minimum efficiency was 14 per cent. This represents (from eq. (4.22) when $a_s = 2d$) a maximum possible feed rate of approximately 2 parts/sec with cylindrical parts of $\frac{5}{16}$ in. diameter.

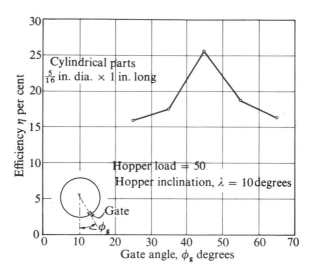

Figure 4.15. Effect of gate angle on efficiency of external gate hopper.

4.5   Rotary Disc Feeder

A typical rotary disc feeder is illustrated in Figure 4.16. This consists of a disc having a number of slots machined radially in its face and mounted at a steep angle to the horizontal, so that it forms the base of a stationary hopper. As the disc rotates, the parts in the hopper are disturbed by the ledges under the slots. Some parts are caught in the slots and carried round until, when each slot in turn reaches the vertical position, it becomes aligned with a delivery chute down which the parts slide. A stationary circular baffle at the centre of the disc prevents the parts sliding out of the slots until they are aligned with the chute.

In some designs of rotary disc feeder the length of the slots will allow more than one part per slot to be selected during each revolution of the disc. This design will be analysed first and it will be assumed that, to give greatest efficiency, the disc is indexed with sufficient dwell to allow all the parts selected in each slot to slide down the chute.

4.5.1   *Indexing Rotary Disc Feeder*

If a Geneva mechanism is employed to index a rotary disc feeder, then the time for index will be approximately equal to the dwell

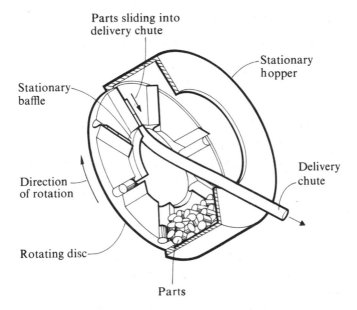

Figure 4.16. Rotary disc feeder.

period. For the design illustrated in Fig. 4.16, the time T_s required for all parts in one slot to slide into the delivery chute is given by:

$$T_s^2 = \frac{2L}{g(\sin \theta - \mu_d \cos \theta)} \qquad (4.25)$$

where L is the length of the slot, θ is the inclination of the delivery chute and μ_d is the coefficient of dynamic friction between the part and the chute.

With a Geneva drive, the total period of indexing, T_i, is therefore given by:

$$T_i = 2T_s = [8L/g(\sin \theta - \mu_d \cos \theta)]^{\frac{1}{2}} \text{ sec.} \qquad (4.26)$$

If l is the length of a part, the maximum number which may be selected in a slot is L/l. However, in practice the average number selected will be less than this. If η is taken to be the 'efficiency' of the feeder, then the feed rate, F_0, will be given by:

$$F_0 = \eta L/l T_i = \eta [Lg(\sin \theta - \mu_d \cos \theta)/8l^2]^{\frac{1}{2}} \qquad (4.27)$$

It can be seen from eq. (4.27) that:

(a) The feed rate is independent of the number of slots in the disc;

(b) For a given feeder the feed rate is inversely proportional to the length of the part;

(c) For maximum feed rate with a given part, μ_d should be as low as possible and both the delivery chute angle, θ, and the slot length, L, should be as large as possible.

It is clear, however, that with the design under consideration, the feed rate will reduce as the hopper gradually empties until, when the hopper is almost empty, no more than one part may be selected in each slot.

4.5.2   Rotary Disc Feeder with Continuous Drive

A rotary disc feeder with continuous drive would be most suitable for feeding disc-shaped parts and, in this case, the analysis for the maximum feed rate would be similar to that for an external gate hopper. With this device the slot length would be equal to the diameter of the part, d, and only one part could be selected in each slot. If the rotational speed of the disc were too high then the parts would pass over the mouth of the delivery chute and feeding would not occur. If the effect of friction is considered negligible because of the large angle of inclination of the disc, then the feed rate at maximum rotational speed will be given by:

$$F_0 = 15 \cdot 8 \eta d^{\frac{1}{2}} \text{ parts/sec} \qquad (4.28)$$

where

$$\eta = \text{efficiency of feeder}$$

$$= \frac{\text{average number of parts selected per cycle}}{\text{number of slots}}$$

The above analyses have considered the theoretical maximum feed rate from a rotary disc feeder both with indexing drive and with continuous drive. The results indicate that the following trends would be expected from this type of feeder:

(a) For an indexing rotary disc feeder with long slots, the maximum feed rate is inversely proportional to the length of the part and proportional to the square root of the slot length.

For high feed rates the slope of the delivery chute should be as large as possible and the coefficient of friction between the part and the chute should be as low as possible;

(b) For a feeder with continuous drive the maximum feed rate for disc shaped parts is inversely proportional to the square root of the diameter of the part.

4.5.3 Load Sensitivity and Efficiency

Tests were conducted on an indexing rotary disc feeder with eight slots, each able to carry two cylindrical parts 1 in. in length and $\frac{5}{16}$ in. in diameter. The results are presented in Fig. 4.17 which shows that, as would be expected, the efficiency reduces as the hopper empties. This is because for small loads, the mass of parts only partly covers the slots and only one part can be selected during

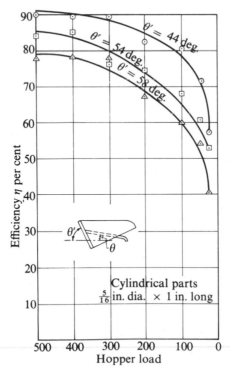

Figure 4.17. Load sensitivity of rotary disc feeder.

each cycle. The figure shows that both the efficiency and the load sensitivity characteristics are improved as the angle of inclination, θ', of the disc is reduced. Unfortunately this also reduces the inclination θ, of the delivery chute and increases the time taken for the parts to slide out of the slots. Clearly in any given design a compromise is necessary and for the design tested the optimum angle of inclination for a load of 100 parts was approximately 56 degrees and the maximum feed rate under these conditions was 3·3 per second.

4.6 Centrifugal Hopper

The centrifugal hopper shown in Fig. 4.18, is particularly suitable for feeding plain cylindrical parts. In this device, the parts are placed in a shallow cylindrical hopper whose base rotates at constant

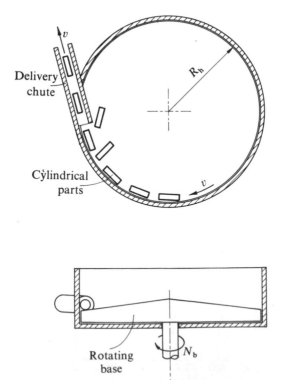

Figure 4.18. Centrifugal hopper.

speed. A delivery chute is arranged tangentially to the stationary wall of the hopper and parts adjacent to this wall which have become correctly oriented, due to the general circulation, pass into the delivery chute. No orienting devices are provided in the hopper and parts must be taken off in the attitude which they naturally adopt in the hopper as indicated in the figure.

4.6.1 Feed Rate

If a part is moving with constant velocity, v, around the inside wall of a centrifugal hopper then the radial reaction at the hopper wall is equal to the centrifugal force $m_p v^2 / R_h$, where m_p is the mass of the part and R_h is the radius of the hopper. The frictional force, F_w, at the hopper wall tends to resist the motion of the part and is given by:

$$F_w = \mu_w m_p v^2 / R_h \qquad (4.29)$$

where μ_w is the coefficient of friction between the part and the hopper wall. When the peripheral velocity of the hopper base is greater than v then the frictional force, F_b, between the part and the rotating hopper base is given by:

$$F_b = \mu_b m_p g \qquad (4.30)$$

where μ_b is the coefficient of friction between the part and the hopper base.

If it is now assumed that $\mu_w = \mu_b$, then since $F_b = F_w$:

$$v = (gR_h)^{\frac{1}{2}} \qquad (4.31)$$

and the maximum feed rate F_{max} of parts of length l is given by:

$$F_{max} = v/l = (gR_h)^{\frac{1}{2}}/l \text{ parts/sec} \qquad (4.32)$$

and the actual feed rate, F_0, may be expressed as

$$F_0 = \eta(gR_h)^{\frac{1}{2}}/l \text{ parts/sec} \qquad (4.33)$$

where η is the feeder efficiency.

Equation (4.33) shows that the unrestricted feed rate from a centrifugal hopper is proportional to the square root of the hopper radius and inversely proportional to the length of the parts.

Equation (4.31) gives the minimum speed of rotation of the hopper base for maximum feed rate.

4.6.2 *Efficiency*

The overall efficiency, η, of the hopper can only be determined by experiment. From eq. (4.32) a 12 in. diameter hopper cannot feed parts 1 in. long at a rate greater than 48 per second.

Using eq. (4.31), the minimum rotational speed, N_b, of the hopper base to give this maximum feed rate is found to be:

$$N_b = 30v/\pi R_h = 30(g/R_h)^{\frac{1}{2}}/\pi = 76 \cdot 6 \text{ rev/min}$$

Tests on an experimental, 12 in. diameter feeder showed that the actual feed rate of $\frac{5}{16}$ in. diameter by 1 in. long parts was 25 per second; this represented an overall efficiency of 52 per cent.

4.7 Revolving Hook Hopper

The revolving hook hopper shown in Fig. 4.19 consists of a hopper in the shape of an inverted truncated cone which is open

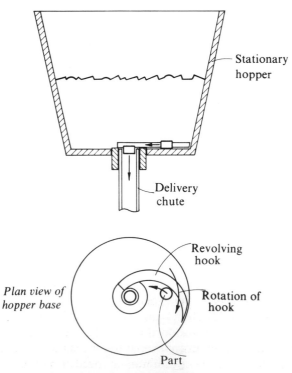

Figure 4.19. Revolving hook hopper.

at the top for parts to be loaded, and closed at the base. The base has a hole in the centre which forms the beginning of the delivery chute. Revolving about the centre of the base and offset so as to clear the hole is a curved wiper blade which extends to the outer edge of the hopper base. Rotation of the hook guides the parts, along the leading edge of the hook, towards the hole at the centre of the hopper and hence to the delivery chute.

4.7.1   Load Sensitivity

With this type of parts feeder, provided the hopper is deep, the loading should have little effect on the feed rate for a wide range of hopper loads.

4.8   Stationary Hook Hopper

This parts feeder (Fig. 4.20) operates on exactly the same principle as the revolving hook hopper, the only difference being that, in this case, the hook is stationary and the base of the hopper rotates slowly. The parts are guided along the edge of the hook towards the periphery of the hopper, where they are eventually deflected into the delivery chute by a deflector mounted on the hopper wall. One advantage of this type of feeder is its gentle feeding action and this makes it suitable for feeding delicate parts at low speed. The feeder is not sensitive to changes in hopper load.

4.9   Paddle Wheel Hopper

In the paddle wheel hopper (Fig. 4.21) the tips of the blades of a vertical multibladed paddle run in a groove in the bottom of the hopper. The groove has dimensions such that the parts in the hopper may be accepted by the groove in one particular attitude only. Rotation of the paddle agitates the parts in the hopper and causes parts arriving at the delivery point in the wrong attitude to be pushed back into the mass of parts.

Experience indicates that, with this type of hopper, the feed rate increases as the hopper empties.

4.10   Tumbling Barrel Hopper

In this hopper (Fig. 4.22), the cylindrical container, which has internal radial fins, rotates about an inclined vibratory feed track. Parts placed in bulk in the hopper are carried upward by the fins

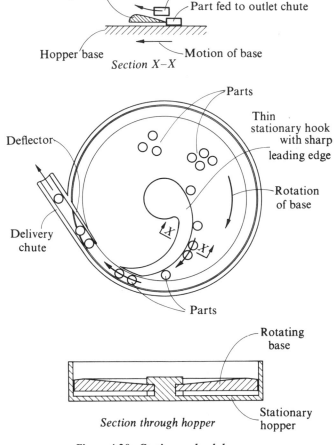

Figure 4.20. Stationary hook hopper.

until at some point they slide off the fin and cascade onto the vibratory feed track. The feed track is shaped to suit the required attitude of the part being fed and only retains and feeds those parts falling in this attitude.

4.11   Rotary Centreboard Hopper

This feeder (Fig. 4.23) consists of a bladed wheel which rotates inside a suitably shaped hopper. The edges of the blades are profiled to collect parts in the desired attitude and lift them clear of the

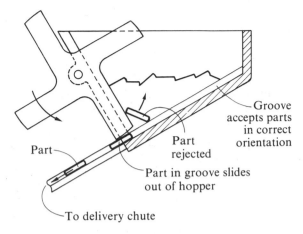

Figure 4.21. Paddle wheel hopper.

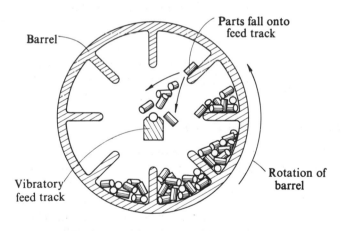

Figure 4.22. Tumbling barrel hopper.

bulk of parts. Further rotation of the wheel causes the oriented parts to slide off the blade which will then be aligned with the delivery chute. It is usual to drive the wheel intermittently by either a Geneva mechanism or a ratchet and pawl mechanism. The design of the indexing mechanism should take into account the dwell time required for a full blade to discharge all its parts when aligned with

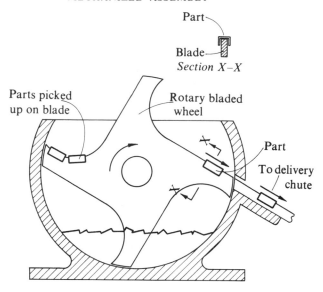

Figure 4.23. Rotary centreboard hopper.

the delivery chute. A similar analysis to that used for the reciprocating centreboard hopper would give the minimum values for dwell and index times and hence the maximum feed rate.

4.12   Magnetic Disc Feeder

This feeder (Fig. 4.24) consists of a sloping container which is closed at its bottom end by a vertical disc. The disc rotates about a horizontal axis and permanent magnets are inserted in pockets around its periphery. As the disc rotates, parts are lifted by the magnets and are stripped off at a convenient point. This feeder only acts as a means of separating parts placed in bulk in the feeder and can clearly only be used for parts of a ferro-magnetic material.

4.13   Elevating Hopper Feeder

This feeder (Fig. 4.25) has a large hopper with inclined sides. Often an agitating device is fitted to the base to encourage the parts to slide to the lowest point in the hopper. An endless conveyor belt fitted with a series of selector ledges, is arranged to elevate parts from the lowest point in the hopper. The ledges are shaped so that

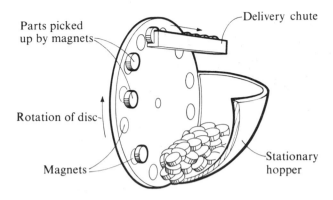

Figure 4.24. Magnetic disc feeder.

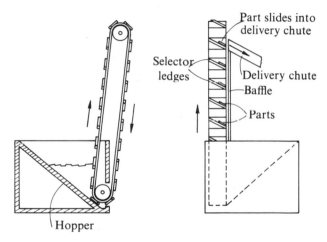

Figure 4.25. Elevating hopper feeder.

they will only accept parts in the desired attitude. The parts slide off the ledges into the delivery chute which is situated at a convenient point above the hopper.

4.14   Magnetic Elevating Hopper Feeder

The magnetic elevating hopper feeder (Fig. 4.26) is basically the same as the elevating hopper feeder except that, instead of ledges, permanent magnets are fitted to the endless belt. Thus the feeder is

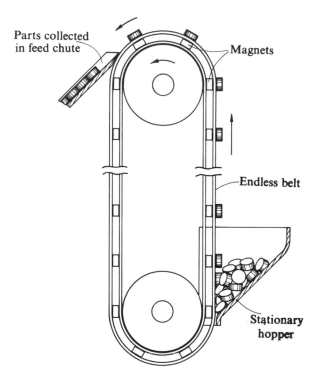

Parts collected in feed chute

Magnets

Endless belt

Stationary hopper

Figure 4.26. Magnetic elevator.

only suitable for handling ferro-magnetic materials and cannot easily be used for orientation purposes. With this feeder, it is usual to strip the parts from the magnets at the top of the belt conveyor.

4.15 Magazines

An alternative means of delivering parts to an automatic assembly machine is from a magazine. With this method parts are stacked into a container or magazine which constrains the parts in the desired orientation. The magazine is then attached directly to the workhead of the assembly machine. The magazines may be spring loaded to facilitate delivery of the parts, or alternatively, the parts may be fed under gravity or assisted from the magazine by compressed air.

Magazines have several advantages over conventional parts feeders and some of these are described below:

(a) In some cases, magazines may be designed to accept only those parts which would be accepted by the assembly machine workhead and thus can act as inspection devices. This can give a considerable reduction in the down-time on the assembly machine;

(b) Magazines can often replace not only the parts feeder but also the feed track;

(c) Magazines are usually very efficient feeding devices and assembly machine down-time due to feeder or feed track blockages can often be eliminated by their use.

Some of the disadvantages associated with the use of magazines are as follows:

(a) Magazines will generally hold considerably fewer parts than the alternative parts feeder and magazine changes must therefore be made more frequently than the refilling of the parts feeder;

(b) The most suitable place to load the magazines is at the point where the part is manufactured since at this point the part is already oriented. When manufacture and assembly take place in the same factory, this may not present a serious problem but if the parts are purchased from another firm it will be much more difficult to arrange for magazine loading.

Some benefits may be obtained if the magazines are loaded at the assembly factory. If a number of similar parts are to be used in an assembly, it may be possible to use one hopper feeder to load all the required magazines. Further, if the magazine is designed to accept only good parts, or some method of inspecting the parts is incorporated into the parts feeder, down time will occur on the magazine loader and not on the assembly machine.

In some cases it is possible to use disposable magazines such as those employed for aspirin tablets. Such a magazine can be rolled up and readily fed to the workhead which would have a suitable mechanism for removing the parts.

Another alternative is where parts are blanked from strip. In this case, the final operation of separating the parts from the strip can be left to the assembly machine workhead.

A further alternative often used for small blanked parts is for the blanking operation to take place on the machine just prior to the point at which the part is required in the assembly.

4.16 Comparison of Feeding Devices

The performance of any feeder is very dependent on the type of part being fed. It is very difficult to make comparisons of the performance and suitability for a given application of the various feeding devices available. Very little research has been conducted on the design and performance of most of the feeders available and it is important that, in the future, sufficient information should become available to allow a choice of the most economic and reliable feeder from a knowledge of the part dimensions, materials, and feed rate required without resorting to experimental investigations.

Reference

1. *Hopper Feeds as an Aid to Automation.* Machinery's Yellowback No. 39, Machinery Publishing Co. Ltd.

5.

Orientation of Parts (Miss Chapter)

In a mechanized assembly machine it is necessary that the parts are fed to the workheads in the correct attitude—in other words, correctly oriented. The devices employed to ensure that only correctly oriented parts are fed to the workhead fall into two groups: those which are incorporated in the parts feeder, which are usually referred to as 'in-bowl' tooling; those which are fitted to the chute between the feeder and the workhead and called 'out-of-bowl' tooling. The devices used for 'in-bowl' tooling very often work on the principle of orienting by rejection and may be termed passive orienting devices. With this type of device only those parts which, by chance, are being fed correctly oriented, pass through the device and the other parts fall back into the hopper or bowl. The rejected parts will then be re-fed and will make a further attempt to pass through the orienting devices. In some cases devices are fitted which re-orient parts. These may be termed active orienting devices and although they are not so widely applicable, they have the advantage that no reduction in feed rate occurs due to the rejection of parts which have already been fed.

Some orienting devices are fitted between the parts feeder and the automatic workhead. Since with this system rejected parts cannot easily be returned to the parts feeder, orienting devices employed in this way are usually of the active type.

In the following a description is given of some of the more common orienting devices and tooling employed in mechanized assembly.

5.1   In-bowl Tooling

Of all the various types of feeding device, vibratory bowl feeders allow by far the greatest flexibility in the design of orienting devices. Figure 5.1 shows the tooling commonly employed to orient screws in a vibratory bowl feeder. In this arrangement the first device, a

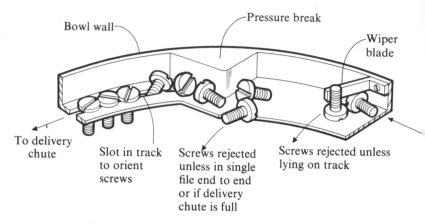

Figure 5.1. Orientation of screws in vibratory bowl feeder.

wiper blade, rejects all the screws not lying flat on the track. The gap below the blade is adjusted so that a screw standing on its head or a screw resting on the top of others will either be deflected back into the bowl or be deflected so that the screw lies flat on the track. Clearly the wiper blade can only be applied here if the length of the screw is greater than the diameter of its head. The next device, a pressure break, will only allow screws to pass in single file with either head or shank leading. Screws being fed in any other attitude will fall off the narrow track and back into the bowl at this point. The pressure break also performs another function; if the delivery chute becomes full, then excess parts will be returned to the bottom of the bowl at the pressure break and congestion will be avoided. The last device consists of a slot in the track which is sufficiently wide to allow the shank of the screw to fall through whilst retaining the screw head. Screws arriving at the slot either with the shank leading or with the head leading will therefore be delivered with the shank down, and supported by the head. In this system for orienting screws, the first two devices are passive and the last is active.

Although the devices described above are designed for a certain shape of part, two of them have wide application in vibratory bowl feeding. A pressure break is usually necessary because most feeders are adjusted to overfeed slightly to ensure that the workhead is never 'starved' of parts. With this situation, and unless a level sensing device controlling the feeder output is attached to the delivery chute, the delivery chute is always full and a pressure break provides a means of preventing congestion at the entrance to the delivery chute. Secondly, the wiper blade is a convenient method of rejecting parts which are resting on top of others. In a vibratory bowl feeder this often occurs because of the pushing action of parts travelling up the track. However, care must be taken in applying the wiper blade because with thin parts there may be a tendency for them to jam under the blade as illustrated in Fig. 5.2. The tendency for this to occur will be reduced by arranging that the blade lies at an acute angle to the bowl as shown in Fig. 5.1. In some cases an alternative approach is necessary and this is illustrated in Fig. 5.3 which shows the tooling commonly employed to orient washers. It can be seen that a portion of the track is arranged to slope sideways and down toward the centre of the bowl. A small ledge is provided along the edge of this section of the track to retain those washers which are lying flat and in single file. Other washers will slide off the track and into the bowl. With a device of this type where the parts are turned as they are fed it is often necessary to arrange the design of the track to ensure that the path of the centre of gravity of the part is not raised rapidly, otherwise a serious reduction in feed rate may occur.

Figure 5.4 shows a refinement to the orienting device described above. In this case machined washers may be oriented by providing a ledge sufficiently large to retain a washer being fed base down (Fig. 5.4a) but too small to retain a washer being fed base up (Fig. 5.4b).

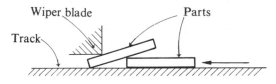

Figure 5.2. Thin parts jammed under wiper blade.

It has been suggested in the past[1] that parts must always be fed in their 'natural resting aspect'. This term is meant to describe the way in which a part will generally come to rest if allowed to fall onto a horizontal surface. Thus, if in a bowl feeder, devices are fitted to reject all parts other than those lying in their 'natural resting aspect', the maximum feed rate of oriented parts will generally be obtained. There are one or two exceptions to this rule, however, and one of these is illustrated by the example in Fig. 5.5. In this case, orienting

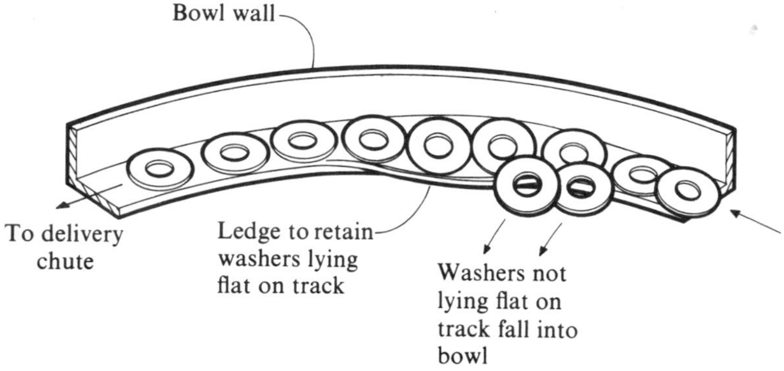

Bowl wall

To delivery chute

Ledge to retain washers lying flat on track

Washers not lying flat on track fall into bowl

Figure 5.3. Orientation of washers in vibratory bowl feeder.

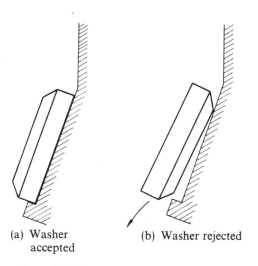

(a) Washer accepted

(b) Washer rejected

Figure 5.4. Orientation of machined washers.

devices suitable for feeding rectangular blocks are shown. Firstly, the width of the track is such that blocks can only be fed with their long axes parallel to the direction of motion. Secondly, a wiper blade is arranged so that blocks lying flat or standing on their sides will be accepted. It is assumed in this example that the width of a block is less than twice its thickness. Finally an active orienting device in the form of a tapered element ensures that blocks lying

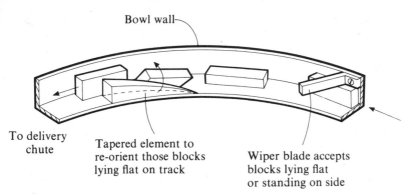

Figure 5.5. Orientation of rectangular blocks in vibratory bowl feeder.

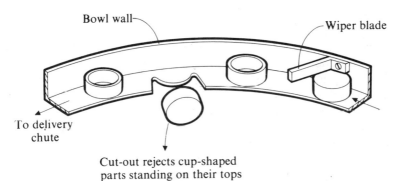

Figure 5.6. Orientation of cup-shaped parts in vibratory bowl feeder.

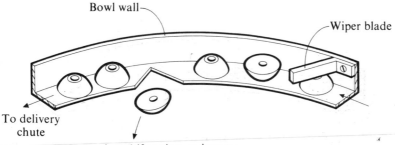

Figure 5.7. Orientation of hemispherical parts in vibratory bowl feeder.

flat will be turned to stand on their sides. With this arrangement all the blocks fed up the track, other than those standing on end, will be fed from the bowl. If, however, the wiper blade had been arranged to accept only the blocks lying flat (in their natural resting aspect) then a large proportion of blocks would have been rejected with a consequent reduction in feed rate.

Figure 5.6 illustrates a common type of orienting device known as a cut-out, where a portion of the track has been cut away. This device makes use of the difference in shape between the top and the base of the part to be fed. Because of the width of the track, and the wiper blade fitted, the cup-shaped part can only arrive at the cut-out resting on its base or on its top. It can be seen from the figure that the cut-out has been designed so that a part resting on its top will fall off the track and into the bowl whereas one resting on its base will pass over the cut-out and move on to the delivery chute.

Figure 5.7 shows another application of a cut-out where the area covered by the top of a part is very much smaller than the area covered by its base. In this case a vee cut-out rejects any part resting on its top. It is interesting to note that this is another example where it is not preferable to feed the parts in their natural resting aspect because in this example it is more convenient to reject those parts which are resting in this position.

Finally, in Fig. 5.8, an example is shown where U-shaped parts are oriented. With parts of this type it is convenient to feed them supported on a rail. In this case a proportion of the parts will climb onto the rail and pass to the delivery chute. The remainder will either fall directly into the bowl or fall into the bowl through a slot between the rail and the bowl wall.

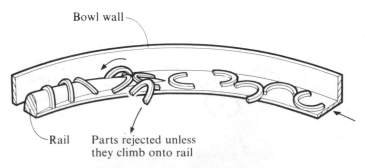

Figure 5.8. Orientation of U-shaped parts in vibratory bowl feeder.

5.2 Effect of Active Orienting Devices on Feed Rate

Sometimes, a part used on an assembly machine will only have a single orientation but more often the number of possible orientations will be considerably greater. If, for example, a part had eight possible orientations and the probabilities of the various orientations were equal and further, if only passive orienting devices were used to orient the parts, the feed rate of oriented parts would be only one-eighth of the actual feed rate. It is clear that if active orienting devices could be utilized the feed rate of oriented parts could be considerably increased.

Work has been carried out by Davies and Sanger[2] on the mechanics of a simple active orienting device. The step orienting device chosen for study (Fig. 5.9) can be specified by one dimension only, namely the step height, h_s. The external shape of the specimen part used in this work was a right cylinder having both length and diameter equal to 0·5 in. The centre of gravity of the part lay on the axis of the cylinder but was displaced from the centre of its axis.

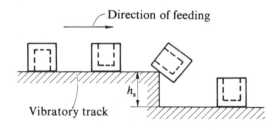

Figure 5.9. Simple step orienting device.

Figure 5.10 shows the six possible orientations of the part. The orientations E and F were not considered in the work since, in practice, they could be filtered out by a passive orienting system. It was found that, for this type of part, the distance between its centre of gravity and the track surface, h_c, and the distance between its centre of gravity and its leading corner, l_c, were the major parameters affecting the behaviour of the part for a given step height. Each of the four orientations A, B, C, and D gave a different value of $l_c - h_c$ and these values are presented in Table 5.1.

Figure 5.11 shows the part in various positions. In position I it is just about to fall over the step in the feed track. In position II, the

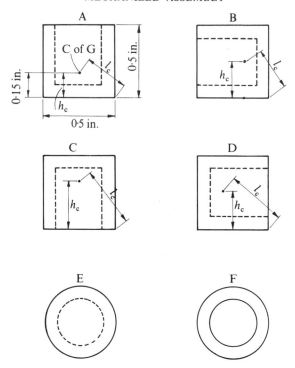

Figure 5.10. Approach attitudes of cup-shaped parts (feeding left to right).

part is stationary and balanced on its leading corner and this is the limiting condition for the part to turn over after negotiating the step. For very low conveying velocities, the initial kinetic energy of the part will be negligible and thus equating its initial and final potential energies and ignoring sliding of the part on the step gives:

$$h_c + h_s = l_c \tag{5.1}$$

where h_s is the step height.

Thus the condition for the part to turn over at least once as it falls off the step is given by:

$$h_s > l_c - h_c \tag{5.2}$$

Figure 5.12 shows the results of tests conducted to observe the effect of the step height, h_s, on the change in orientation of the part. It can be seen that with parts approaching the step in orientation A,

TABLE 5.1

Values of $l_c - h_c$ for the Part used in the Experiments

Orientation	$(l_c - h_c)$ in.
A	0·14
B	0·04
C	0·08
D	0·18

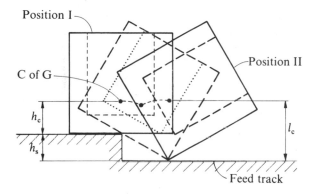

Figure 5.11. Motion of part on a step orienting device.

no re-orientation occurs unless the step height exceeds 0·3 in. For step heights exceeding 0·53 in., all the parts arriving in orientation A are turned over into orientation D. Intermediate values of the step height result in varying proportions of the two orientations A and D and at a step height of approximately 0·41 in., 50 per cent of the parts arriving in orientation A are turned over into orientation D. The remaining curves in Fig. 5.12 illustrate the behaviour of parts arriving in the remaining orientations B, C, and D. The vertical lines shown on the figures represent a step height of $l_c - h_c$ which is the limiting condition given by eq. (5.2). It is clear that for approach orientations B and C this value of step height gives a good indication of the point at which the device begins to have an effect. However,

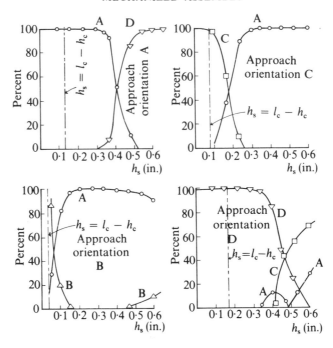

Figure 5.12. Performance of a simple step orienting device. (After Davies and Sanger[2]*.)*

for approach orientations A and D, the step height given by eq. (5.2) is considerably smaller than the value at which the device begins to affect the orientation of the part. This is because, for large values of $l_c - h_c$, frictional effects should be taken into account in the derivation of the limiting conditions.

It is now possible, from Fig. 5.12, to determine the output distribution of the parts in the various orientations if the distribution of input orientations is known. It can be seen from the results that with a step height of 0·3 in. and an even distribution of parts arriving in orientations A, B, C, and D, 75 per cent of the parts would leave the device in orientation A and the remaining 25 per cent in orientation D. Thus, with a final passive orienting device designed to reject all parts except those in orientation A, the final output of oriented parts would be 200 per cent greater than the output obtained with purely passive devices.

5.3 Out-of-bowl Tooling

A further type of orienting device is that which is situated between the feeder and the workhead. Such devices are usually of the active type because orientation by rejection is not often practicable. Figure 5.13 illustrates a device described by Tipping[3] where the position of the centre of gravity of a part is utilized. In this example the cup-shaped part is pushed onto a bridge and the weight of the part acting through the centre of gravity pulls the part down nose first into the delivery chute regardless of its initial orientation. In Fig. 5.14 the same part is re-oriented using a different principle. With this method, if the part passes nose first down the delivery tube it is deflected directly into the delivery chute and maintains its original orientation. A part fed open-end first will be re-oriented by the pin located in the wall of the device.

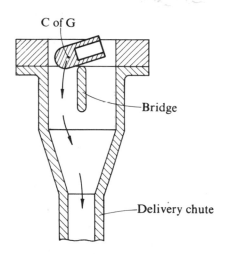

Figure 5.13. Reorientation of cup-shaped part. (After Tipping[3].)

The device illustrated in Fig. 5.15 is known as a selector and employs a principle which has been successfully applied to re-orient a wide variety of parts[4]. The selector consists of a stationary container in which is mounted a wheel with radial slots. The wheel is driven by an indexing mechanism in order to ensure that the slots

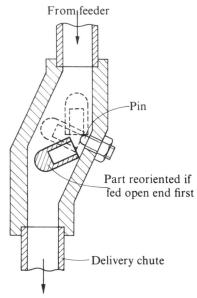

From feeder

Pin

Part reoriented if
fed open end first

Delivery chute

Figure 5.14. Reorientation of cup-shaped part. (After Tipping[3].)

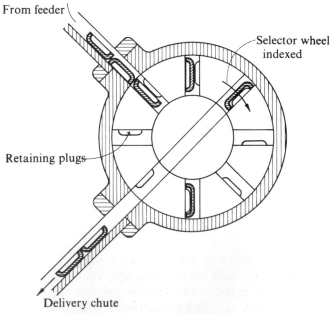

From feeder

Selector wheel
indexed

Retaining plugs

Delivery chute

Figure 5.15. Reorientation of shallow-drawn parts. (After (4).)

always align with the chutes. In the design illustrated the shallow-drawn parts may enter the slot in the selector wheel in either of two attitudes. After two indexes the parts are aligned with the delivery chute and those which now lie open end upward, slide out of the selector and into the delivery chute. Those which lie open end downward are retained by a plug in the slot. After a further four indexes the slot is again aligned with the delivery chute. The part has now been turned over and is free to slide into the delivery chute.

References

1. TIPPING, W. V. 'Mechanised Assembly.' Paper presented to the Society of Engineers, 26 April, 1965.
2. DAVIES, P. B. and SANGER, D. J. 'The Characteristics of a Simple Orienting Device.' Paper presented at the Conference on Mechanized Assembly, July 1966, Royal College of Advanced Technology, Salford.
3. TIPPING, W. V. 'Mechanised Assembly Machines, 9—Orientation and Selection.' *Machine Design Engineering*, February, 1966, p. 38.
4. *Hopper Feeds as an Aid to Automation*. Machinery's Yellowback No. 39, Machinery Publishing Co. Ltd.

6.

Feed Tracks, Escapements, and Parts Placing Mechanisms

To provide easy access to automatic workheads and the assembly machine generally, the parts feeder is usually placed some distance away from the workhead. The parts have, therefore, to be transferred and maintained in orientation between the feeder and the workhead by use of a *feed track*. Most parts feeders do not supply parts at the discrete intervals usually required by an automatic workhead. As a result, the parts feeder must be adjusted to overfeed slightly and some metering device, usually referred to as an *escapement*, is necessary to ensure that parts arrive at the automatic workhead at the correct intervals. After leaving the escapement, the parts are then placed in the assembly; a process usually carried out by a *parts placing mechanism*.

6.1 Gravity Feed Track Arrangements

Feed tracks may be classified as either gravity tracks or powered tracks. By far the majority of tracks are of the gravity type and these may take many forms. Two typical track arrangements are illustrated in Fig. 6.1; the choice of design generally depends on the required direction of entry of the part into the workhead. In design it should be remembered that the track may not always be full and it is desirable that feeding should still take place under this condition.

When the track is partly full and no pushing action is obtained by air jets or vibration it is clear that the vertical delivery track design shown in Fig. 6.1b will deliver parts from rest at a greater rate than the horizontal delivery design shown in Fig. 6.1a. The performance of the vertical delivery track will also be independent of the loading in the track and if no further parts are fed into the track it will deliver the last part as quickly as the first. The time of delivery, t_p,

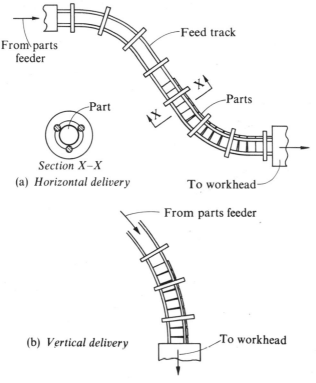

From parts
feeder

Feed track

Part

Parts

Section X–X

(a) *Horizontal delivery*

To workhead

From parts feeder

(b) *Vertical delivery*

To workhead

Figure 6.1. *Gravity feed track arrangements.*

will be given by the time taken for a part to fall a distance equal to its own length.

Thus

$$t_p^2 = 2l/g \qquad (6.1)$$

where l is the length of the part.

6.1.1   *Analysis of Horizontal Delivery Feed Track*

In the track design for feeding horizontally (Fig. 6.1a), the last few parts cannot be fed and even if the height of parts in the track is maintained at a given level, the delivery time will be greater than that given by eq. (6.1).

Figure 6.2 shows the basic parameters defining the last portion of a horizontal delivery feed track. This consists of a horizontal section,

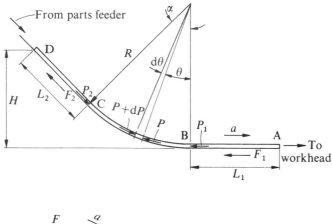

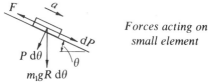

Forces acting on
small element

Figure 6.2. Idealized horizontal delivery gravity track.

AB, of length L_1, preceded by a curved portion, BC, of constant radius, R, which in turn is preceded by a straight portion inclined at an angle α to the horizontal. It will be assumed in the following analysis that the level of parts in the track is maintained at a height, H, above the delivery point. If the length of the straight inclined portion of the track containing parts is denoted by L_2 then

$$H = L_2 \sin \alpha + R(1 - \cos \alpha) \qquad (6.2)$$

An equation is now derived giving the time, t_p, to deliver one part of length l. It is assumed in the analysis that the length of each part is small compared with the dimensions of the feed track and that the column of parts can be treated as a continuous infinitely flexible rod.

When the restraining force at A is removed, the column of parts will start to slide forward. In calculating the acceleration, a, of the column of parts it is necessary to consider the parts in the three sections of the track AB, BC, and CD separately.

If the mass per unit length of the column of parts is denoted by m_1 then the weight of section AB will be given by m_1L_1g and the total frictional resistance, F_1, in this region will be given by

$$F_1 = \mu_d m_1 L_1 g \tag{6.3}$$

where μ_d is the coefficient of friction between the parts and the track.

The equation of motion for section AB is now given by

$$P_1 = F_1 + m_1 L_1 a = m_1 L_1 (\mu_d g + a) \tag{6.4}$$

where P_1 is the force exerted on the parts in section AB by the remainder of the parts in the feed track and a is the initial acceleration of the parts.

Similarly the column of parts in the straight inclined portion, DC, of the feed track will be partly restrained by a force P_2 given by

$$m_1 L_2 g \sin \alpha - P_2 = F_2 + m_1 L_2 a \tag{6.5}$$

where F_2 is the total frictional resistance in this section.

Since

$$F_2 = \mu_d m_1 L_2 g \cos \alpha$$

then

$$P_2 = m_1 L_2 (g \sin \alpha - \mu_d g \cos \alpha - a) \tag{6.6}$$

To analyse the motion of the parts in the curved section, BC, of the feed track, it is necessary to consider an element of length $R\,d\theta$ on a portion of the track which is inclined at an angle θ to the horizontal. In this case a force P is resisting the motion of the element and a force $(P + dP)$ is tending to accelerate the element. These forces have a small component $P\,d\theta$ which increases the reaction between the parts and the track.

The external forces acting on the element are shown in the figure and the equation of motion is:

$$m_1 g R \sin \theta \, d\theta + dP = F + m_1 R a \, d\theta$$

and since

$$F = \mu_d (m_1 g R \cos \theta \, d\theta + P \, d\theta)$$

then

$$dP = m_1 g R(a/g + \mu_d \cos \theta - \sin \theta) \, d\theta + \mu_d P \, d\theta \tag{6.7}$$

When $\theta = 0$, $P = P_1$,

thus:

$$\int_{P_1}^{P} dP = m_l g R \int_0^{\theta} \left(\frac{a}{g} + \mu_d \cos \theta - \sin \theta \right) d\theta + \mu_d \int_0^{\theta} P \, d\theta$$

or

$$P = P_1 + m_l g R \left(\frac{a\theta}{g} + \mu_d \sin \theta + \cos \theta - 1 \right) + \mu_d \int_0^{\theta} P \, d\theta$$

(6.8)

The general expression for P may be obtained by repeated substitution of eq. (6.8) in the last term of this equation. Thus:

$$P = Z + \mu_d \int_0^{\theta} Z \, d\theta + \mu_d^2 \int_0^{\theta} \int_0^{\theta} Z \, d\theta \, d\theta + \mu_d^3 \int_0^{\theta} \int_0^{\theta} \int_0^{\theta} Z \, d\theta \, d\theta \, d\theta + \dots$$

(6.9)

where

$$Z = P_1 + m_l g R \left(\frac{a\theta}{g} + \mu_d \sin \theta + \cos \theta - 1 \right)$$

Therefore:

$$
\begin{aligned}
P = & \left[P_1 + m_l g R \left\{ \frac{a\theta}{g} + \mu_d \sin \theta - (1 - \cos \theta) \right\} \right] \\
& + \mu_d \left[P_1 \theta + m_l g R \left\{ \frac{a\theta^2}{g2!} + \mu_d(1 - \cos \theta) - \theta + \sin \theta \right\} \right] \\
& + \mu_d^2 \left[P_1 \frac{\theta^2}{2!} + m_l g R \left\{ \frac{a\theta^3}{g3!} + \mu_d \theta - \mu_d \sin \theta - \frac{\theta^2}{2!} + (1 - \cos \theta) \right\} \right] \\
& + \mu_d^3 \left[P_1 \frac{\theta^3}{3!} + m_l g R \left\{ \frac{a\theta^4}{g4!} + \mu_d \frac{\theta^2}{2!} - \mu_d(1 - \cos \theta) - \frac{\theta^3}{3!} \right. \right. \\
& \left. \left. \qquad\qquad\qquad\qquad\qquad + \theta - \sin \theta \right\} \right] \\
& + \mu_d^4 \left[P_1 \frac{\theta^4}{4!} + m_l g R \left\{ \frac{a\theta^5}{g5!} + \mu_d \frac{\theta^3}{3!} - \mu_d \theta + \mu_d \sin \theta - \frac{\theta^4}{4!} \right. \right. \\
& \left. \left. \qquad\qquad\qquad\qquad\qquad + \frac{\theta^2}{2!} - (1 - \cos \theta) \right\} \right]
\end{aligned}
$$

$$+ \mu_d^5 \left[P_1 \frac{\theta^5}{5!} + m_l g R \left\{ \frac{a\theta^6}{g6!} + \mu_d \frac{\theta^4}{4!} - \mu_d \frac{\theta^2}{2!} + \mu_d(1 - \cos\theta) \right. \right.$$

$$\left. \left. - \frac{\theta^5}{5!} + \frac{\theta^3}{3!} - \theta + \sin\theta \right\} \right]$$

$$+ \ldots \tag{6.10}$$

collecting like terms:

$$P = P_1 \left(1 + \mu_d\theta + \frac{\mu_d^2\theta^2}{2!} + \frac{\mu_d^3\theta^3}{3!} + \ldots \right)$$

$$+ \frac{m_l Ra}{\mu_d} \left(\mu_d\theta + \frac{\mu_d^2\theta^2}{2!} + \frac{\mu_d^3\theta^3}{3!} + \frac{\mu_d^4\theta^4}{4!} + \ldots \right)$$

$$+ m_l g R \sin\theta (2\mu_d - 2\mu_d^3 + 2\mu_d^5 - \ldots)$$

$$+ m_l g R \cos\theta (1 - 2\mu_d^2 + 2\mu_d^4 - 2\mu_d^6 + \ldots)$$

$$+ m_l g R(-1 + 2\mu_d^2 - 2\mu_d^4 + 2\mu_d^6 - \ldots)$$

$$- m_l g R \left(\mu_d\theta + \frac{\mu_d^2\theta^2}{2!} + \frac{\mu_d^3\theta^3}{3!} + \frac{\mu_d^4\theta^4}{4!} + \ldots \right)$$

$$\times (1 - 2\mu_d^2 + 2\mu_d^4 - \ldots) \tag{6.11}$$

Now since

$$e^{\mu_d\theta} = 1 + \mu_d\theta + \frac{\mu_d^2\theta^2}{2!} + \frac{\mu_d^3\theta^3}{3!} + \ldots \text{ for all values of } \mu_d\theta$$

and

$$\frac{1}{1 + \mu_d^2} = 1 - \mu_d^2 + \mu_d^4 - \mu_d^6 + \ldots \text{ when } \mu_d < 1\cdot0$$

equation (6.11) becomes

$$P = P_1 e^{\mu_d\theta} + \frac{m_l Ra}{\mu_d}(e^{\mu_d\theta} - 1) + \frac{m_l g R}{1 + \mu_d^2}[2\mu_d \sin\theta + (1 - \mu_d^2)$$

$$\times (\cos\theta - e^{\mu_d\theta})] \tag{6.12}$$

Now writing $\theta = \alpha$ and $P = P_2$, substituting for P_1 and P_2 from eqs. (6.4) and (6.6) and re-arranging:

$$\frac{a}{g} = \frac{L_2(\sin \alpha - \mu_d \cos \alpha) - L_1 \mu_d \, e^{\mu_d \alpha} + [R/(1 + \mu_d^2)] \times [(1 - \mu_d^2)(e^{\mu_d \alpha} - \cos \alpha) - 2\mu_d \sin \alpha]}{L_2 + L_1 \, e^{\mu_d \alpha} + (R/\mu_d)(e^{\mu_d \alpha} - 1)}$$

(6.13)

If the length of each part, l, is small compared with the total length of the column of parts then it may be assumed that the acceleration a will be constant during the delivery of one part.

Thus

$$t_p^2 = 2l/a \tag{6.14}$$

where t_p is the time taken to deliver one part and a is the acceleration of the column of parts obtained from eq. (6.13).

If the various parameters are such that the numerator of eq. (6.13) becomes zero then the parts will not feed. Thus, for feeding to occur:

$$L_2(\sin \alpha - \mu_s \cos \alpha) + \frac{R}{(1 + \mu_s^2)}$$

$$\times [(1 - \mu_s^2)(e^{\mu_s \alpha} - \cos \alpha) - 2\mu_s \sin \alpha] > L_1 \mu_s \, e^{\mu_s \alpha} \tag{6.15}$$

It can also be deduced from eq. (6.13) that for high accelerations and thus short delivery times, L_1, R, and μ_d should be small and L_2 and α should be large.

It should be pointed out that eq. (6.7), which is a first-order differential equation, may be more readily solved by the use of the operator, D. Equation (6.7) may be re-written as follows:

$$(D - \mu_d)P = m_l g R(a/g + \mu_d \cos \theta - \sin \theta) \tag{6.16}$$

The complementary function is given by:

$$\text{C.F.} = A \, e^{\mu_d \theta} \tag{6.17}$$

and the particular integral:

$$\text{P.I.} = m_l g R \left[\left(\frac{D + \mu_d}{D^2 - \mu_d^2} \right) \cdot (\mu_d \cos \theta - \sin \theta) - \frac{1}{\mu_d(1 - D/\mu_d)} \cdot \frac{a}{g} \right]$$

$$= m_l g R \left[\left(\frac{D + \mu_d}{1 + \mu_d^2} \right) \cdot (\sin \theta - \mu_d \cos \theta) - \frac{a}{\mu_d g} \right]$$

$$= m_l g R \left[\left(\frac{1 - \mu_d^2}{1 + \mu_d^2} \right) \cos \theta + \frac{2\mu_d \sin \theta}{(1 + \mu_d^2)} - \frac{a}{\mu_d g} \right] \tag{6.18}$$

The general solution is now given by the sum of expressions (6.17) and (6.18). Thus:

$$P = A\, e^{\mu_d \theta} + m_1 g R \left[\frac{(1 - \mu_d^2)\cos\theta + 2\mu_d \sin\theta}{(1 + \mu_d^2)} - \frac{a}{\mu_d g} \right] \qquad (6.19)$$

When $\theta = 0$, $P = P_1$ and therefore the constant A is found to be:

$$A = P_1 - m_1 g R \left[\left(\frac{1 - \mu_d^2}{1 + \mu_d^2} \right) - \frac{a}{\mu_d g} \right] \qquad (6.20)$$

Substitution of eq. (6.20) in eq. (6.19) gives, after rearrangement:

$$P = P_1\, e^{\mu_d \theta} + \frac{m_1 R a}{\mu_d}(e^{\mu_d \theta} - 1) + \frac{m_1 g R}{(1 + \mu_d^2)}$$
$$\times [2\mu_d \sin\theta + (1 - \mu_d^2)(\cos\theta - e^{\mu_d \theta})]$$

which is identical to eq. (6.12) above.

6.1.2 Example

A horizontal delivery feed track is designed so that $L_1 = 0$, $R = 6$ in. and $\alpha = 45$ degrees. The delivery time of a 1 in. long part having a coefficient of dynamic friction of 0·2 may be obtained as follows:

From eq. (6.13),

$$\frac{a}{g} = \frac{L_2(0.707 \times 0.8) + (6/1.04)[0.96 \times (1.17 - 0.707) - 0.4 \times 0.707]}{L_2 + (6/0.2)(1.17 - 1.0)}$$

Therefore

$$\frac{a}{g} = \frac{0.566 L_2 + 0.935}{L_2 + 5.1}$$

and from eq. (6.14):

$$t_p^2 = \frac{2l}{a} = \frac{2(L_2 + 5.1)}{(0.566 L_2 + 0.935)32.2 \times 12} = \frac{5.1 + L_2}{181 + 109 L_2} \sec^2$$

If a delivery time of 0·1 sec is required then L_2 is given by:

$$181 + 109 L_2 = 10^2 (5.1 + L_2)$$

or

$$L_2 = 36.5 \text{ in.}$$

From eq. (6.2), therefore, the required height of the parts above the track outlet is given by:

$$H = 36\cdot5 \times 0\cdot707 + 6(1 - 0\cdot707) = 27\cdot5 \text{ in.}$$

With a vertical delivery feed track, the delivery time is found from eq. (6.1) to be $0\cdot072$ sec and is independent of the level of parts in the track.

More general results for a horizontal delivery gravity feed track are given in Fig. 6.3 where $L_1 = 0$, $R = 6$ in., $\alpha = 45$ degrees and $l = 1$ in. The height of the column of parts, H, is plotted against t_p, the time taken to deliver one part, for three values of the coefficient of friction between the parts and the track. It is clear from the figure that if the height of the column of parts falls below 10 in., this results in large differences between the times taken to deliver one part for the various frictional conditions and for the high coefficient of friction, the time taken to deliver one part increases very rapidly.

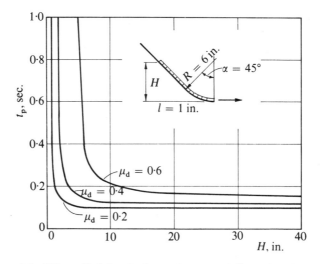

Figure 6.3. *Effect of height of column of parts on delivery time for a horizontal delivery gravity feed track.*

6.1.3 Feed Track Section

A compromise is necessary when designing the feed track section. The clearances between the part and the track must be sufficiently large to allow transfer and yet must be small enough to prevent the part losing its orientation during transfer. In the curved portions of the track further allowances have to be made to prevent the part jamming. Figure 6.4 shows a cylindrical part in a curved tubular track. For the part to negotiate the bend the minimum track diameter, D_t, is given by:

$$D_t = c + d \qquad (6.21)$$

and by geometry;

$$c(2(R + D_t) - c) = (l/2)^2$$

where R is the inside radius of the curved track and l is the length of the part. If c is small compared with $2(R + D_t)$ then this equation becomes:

$$2c(R + D_t) = (l/2)^2 \text{ approximately} \qquad (6.22)$$

Substituting for c from eq. (6.22) in eq. (6.21) and re-arranging gives:

$$D_t = 0 \cdot 5\{[(R + d)^2 + (l/2)^2]^{\frac{1}{2}} - (R - d)\} \qquad (6.23)$$

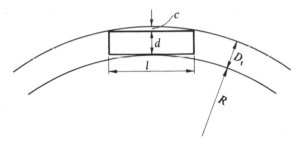

Figure 6.4. Construction to determine minimum diameter of curved feed track.

If the parts are sufficiently bent or 'bowed' then it may be difficult to design a curved track which will not allow overlapping of parts and consequent jamming. This is illustrated in Fig. 6.5.

Figure 6.6 illustrates typical track sections used for transferring cylinders, flat plates, and headed parts. An important point to be remembered when designing a feed track is that the effective co-efficient of friction between the parts and the track may be higher than the actual coefficient of friction between the two materials. Figure 6.7 gives some examples of the effect of track cross-section on the effective coefficient of friction. The increase of 100 per cent

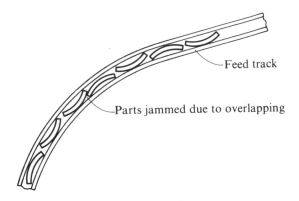

Figure 6.5. Blockage in curved feed track.

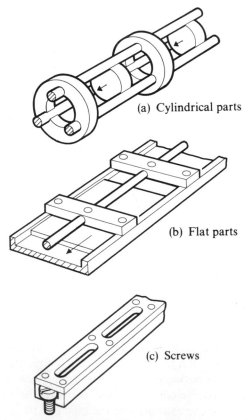

(a) Cylindrical parts

(b) Flat parts

(c) Screws

Figure 6.6. Various gravity feed track sections for typical parts.

in friction given by the example in Fig. 6.7d could have very serious consequences in a gravity feed system.

6.1.4   Feeding of Headed Parts

Of the many types of part which are fed in a gravity feed track, perhaps the most common are headed parts such as screws and rivets which are usually fed in the manner shown in Fig. 6.6. As the track inclination, θ, is gradually increased from zero, the part will start to slide when $\tan \theta > \mu_s$. As the track angle, θ, is increased further, and if the depth of the track, D_a, is greater than the height of the head, h, the condition shown in Fig. 6.8 will eventually arise. Here, the corner **B** of the head has just made contact with the lower surface of the top of the track. Under these conditions, the centre

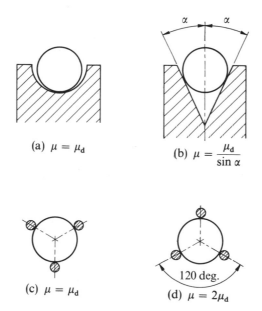

(a) $\mu = \mu_d$

(b) $\mu = \dfrac{\mu_d}{\sin \alpha}$

(c) $\mu = \mu_d$

(d) $\mu = 2\mu_d$

Figure 6.7. Relation between effective coefficient of friction μ and actual coefficient of dynamic friction μ_d for various track designs.

of gravity of the part lies directly below **A**. Thus, from the triangle ACD:

$$d/2l_g = \tan(\theta_T - \alpha_p) \tag{6.24}$$

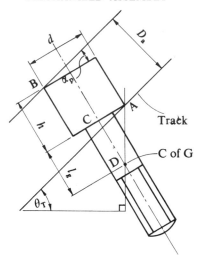

Figure 6.8. *Position of headed part when corner B just contacts the lower surface of the track top.*

where θ_T is the track angle at which the above condition arises. Now

$$D_a = d \sin \alpha_p + h \cos \alpha_p \qquad (6.25)$$

and combining eqs. (6.24) and (6.25) gives:

$$\tan \theta_T = \frac{(d^2 - 2l_g h) \cos \alpha_p + 2l_g D_a}{d(2l_g + h) \cos \alpha_p - D_a d} \qquad (6.26)$$

where

$$\cos \alpha_p = \frac{D_a h + d(d^2 + h^2 - D_a^2)^{\frac{1}{2}}}{h^2 + d^2} \qquad (6.27)$$

If μ_s is the coefficient of static friction between the part and the track then sliding will always occur if $\tan \theta_T > \tan \theta > \mu_s$. Sliding may occur, however, if $\tan \theta$ is increased above the value given by eq. (6.26). The situation in this case is shown in Fig. 6.9 where frictional forces arise at corners A and B of the screw head.

For sliding to occur under these circumstances,

$$m_p g \sin \theta > F_1 + F_2 \qquad (6.28)$$

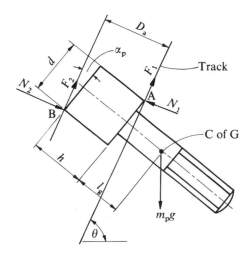

Figure 6.9. Forces acting on headed part sliding down an inclined track.

Now

and

$$F_1 = \mu_s N_1 \atop F_2 = \mu_s N_2 \Big\} \qquad (6.29)$$

And resolving forces normal to the track gives:

$$N_1 = N_2 + m_p g \cos \theta \qquad (6.30)$$

Finally, taking moments about A gives:

$$m_p g(l_g \sin(\theta - \alpha_p) - (d/2) \cos(\theta - \alpha_p))$$
$$= N_2(d \cos \alpha_p - h \sin \alpha_p) - F_2 D_a$$

which becomes, after re-arrangement:

$$N_2 = \frac{m_p g[l_g \sin(\theta - \alpha_p) - (d/2) \cos(\theta - \alpha_p)]}{d \cos \alpha_p - h \sin \alpha_p - \mu_s D_a} \qquad (6.31)$$

Equations (6.28), (6.29), (6.30), and (6.31) may now be combined to give the upper value of $\tan \theta$ for sliding to occur. Thus:

$$\tan \theta < \frac{\mu_s D_a(\mu_s d + 2l_g + h) - \mu_s h \cos \alpha_p(2l_g + h)}{\cos \alpha_p(\mu_s d(2l_g + h) - h^2 - d^2) + hD_a} \qquad (6.32)$$

where $\cos \alpha_p$ is given by eq. (6.27).

Equation (6.32) will be true for $\theta < 90$ degrees since the numerator of the right-hand side of this expression will always be positive and the denominator must necessarily be positive for $\theta < 90$ degrees. Equation (6.32) may be expressed non-dimensionally by dividing the numerator and denominator by h^2 and writing

$$d/h = d_0, \quad l_g/h = l_0 \quad \text{and} \quad D_a/h = D_0.$$

Thus, for sliding to take place:

$$\mu_s < \tan \theta < \frac{\mu_s D_0(\mu_s d_0 + 2l_0 + 1) - \mu_s(2l_0 + 1)\cos \alpha_p}{\cos \alpha_p(\mu_s d_0(2l_0 + 1) - 1 - d_0^2) + D_0} \quad (6.33)$$

when $\theta > \theta_T$.

Also, the equation for θ_T may be written as:

$$\tan \theta_T = \frac{(d_0^2 - 2l_0)\cos \alpha_p + 2l_0 D_0}{d_0(2l_0 + 1)\cos \alpha_p - D_0 d_0} \quad (6.34)$$

where

$$\cos \alpha_p = \frac{D_0 + d_0(d_0^2 + 1 - D_0^2)^{\frac{1}{2}}}{1 + d_0^2} \quad (6.35)$$

Figure 6.10 shows a graph of θ plotted against D_0 for values of $l_0 = 1 \cdot 5$ and $d_0 = 1$ and for various values of the coefficient of static friction between the part and the track. The line X—X shows the values of θ_T given by eq. (6.34) and therefore indicates, for various clearances between the part and the track, the value of θ at which the point B in Fig. 6.8 makes contact with the track. For track angles below this value and above the value for the corresponding value of μ_s the part will always slide. Once the value of θ exceeds θ_T, the limiting condition for sliding to occur is given by eq. (6.33). The curves for various values of μ_s are shown in the figure. It is clear that for large values of μ_s, the range of track angles and clearances where sliding will take place is limited. Further, under these circumstances, very large track angles and large clearances are necessary.

It is important to note that for a wide range of practical conditions, headed parts of the type shown will not slide when the track angle is very large or very small. Thus, the designer must consider track angles and clearances carefully in order to avoid subsequent parts transfer problems.

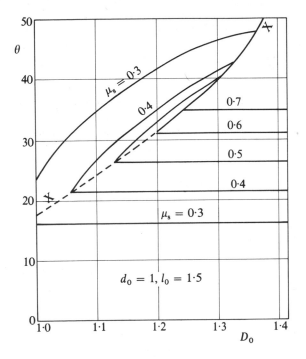

Figure 6.10. Effect of dimensionless track depth, D_0, and track angle, θ, on the limiting conditions for sliding of a headed part.

Whilst the gravity feed track is the simplest form of feed track it has some disadvantages. The main disadvantage is the need to have the feeder in an elevated position. This may cause trouble in loading the feeder and in freeing any blockages which may occur. In such cases the use of a powered track may be considered.

6.2   Powered Feed Tracks

The most common types of powered feed track are vibratory tracks and air-assisted tracks. A vibratory feed track is illustrated in Fig. 6.11 and operates on the same principle as the vibratory bowl feeder (see chapter 3 and appendix I). With this device, the track is generally horizontal and its performance is subject to many of the limitations of a conventional vibratory bowl feeder. In the feeder shown the vibrations normal and parallel to the track are 'in-phase' and the feeding characteristics will be affected by changes in the

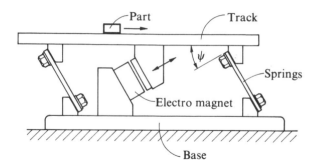

Figure 6.11. Horizontal vibratory feed track.

effective coefficient of friction, μ between the parts and the track. This is illustrated in Fig. 3.10 where it can be seen that an increase in μ generally gives an increase in the conveying velocity. For example, a typical operating condition would be where the normal track acceleration, $A_n = 1 \cdot 1\, g_n$. In this case stable feeding would occur and a change in μ from $0 \cdot 2$ to $0 \cdot 8$ would give an increase in conveying velocity from $0 \cdot 8$ to $2 \cdot 2$ in/sec when operating at a frequency of 50 c/s. It is shown in Appendix I that introducing the appropriate phase difference between the components of vibration normal and parallel to the track can give conditions where the conveying velocity is consistently high for a wide range of values of μ. With a track inclined at 4 degrees to the horizontal (a typical figure for a bowl feeder) the optimum phase angle for a normal track acceleration of $1 \cdot 2g$ is approximately 65 degrees. Figure I.3 shows that this figure is not significantly affected by the vibration angle employed. In the work which led to these results it was also found that the optimum phase angle reduces as the track angle is reduced until, when the track is inclined downward at an angle of 8 degrees the optimum phase angle is almost zero. This means that a drive of the type shown in Fig. 6.11 operates under almost optimum conditions for a track inclined at 8 degrees downward. Under these circumstances the mean conveying velocity for a wide range of μ will be given by:

$$v_m = 175/f \text{ in/sec} \qquad (6.36)$$

where f is the frequency of vibration, c/s, and when the vibration angle is 20 degrees and $A_n/g_n = 1 \cdot 2$. In this case, the mean conveying velocity for an operating frequency of 50 c/s would be $3 \cdot 5$ in/sec. A higher feed rate could be obtained by reducing the vibration angle, increasing the downward slope of the track or reducing the frequency of vibration.

For downward sloping tracks with a large inclination, large feed rates can be obtained with zero vibration angle. In this case the track is simply vibrated parallel to itself and typical feeding characteristics thus obtained are illustrated in Fig. 6.12 which shows the effect of parallel track acceleration on the mean conveying velocity

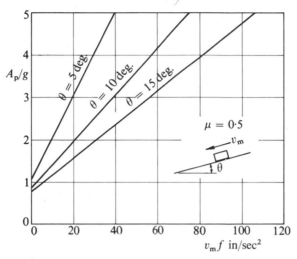

Figure 6.12. Effect of parallel track acceleration on mean conveying velocity.

for various track angles when the coefficient of friction is 0·5. The results for a feed track with parallel vibration can be summarized by the empirical equation

$$v_m = \frac{(\theta/f)(A_p/g + 9 \cdot 25\theta^2/10^4 - 2 \cdot 3\mu + 0 \cdot 25)}{0 \cdot 007\theta + 0 \cdot 07 + 0 \cdot 8\mu} \qquad (6.37)$$

where

v_m = mean conveying velocity, in/sec
f = vibration frequency, c/s
θ = inclination of downward sloping track, degrees
μ = effective coefficient of friction between part and track
A_p = parallel track acceleration

Equation (6.37) applies when $A_p/g \geqslant 2 \cdot 0$, $0 \cdot 3 \leqslant \mu \leqslant 0 \cdot 8$, $5 \leqslant \theta \leqslant 25$ and when $\theta \leqslant 28 \cdot 5 \mu + 2 \cdot 5$.

6.2.1 *Example*

A track inclined downward at 10 degrees is vibrated parallel to itself at a frequency of 50 c/s with an amplitude of vibration of 0·01 in. If the coefficient of friction between the part and the track is 0·5, the mean conveying velocity of the part may be estimated as follows:

The dimensionless parallel track acceleration

$$A_p/g = \frac{0·01(2\pi \times 50)^2}{32·2 \times 12} = 2·55$$

Since $\theta < 28·5\mu + 2·5$ and $A_p/g > 2·0$ eq. (6.37) applies and therefore:

$$v_m = \frac{(10/50)(2·55 + 9·25/10^2 - 1·15 + 0·25)}{0·07 + 0·07 + 0·4} = 0·644 \text{ in/sec}$$

If a conveying velocity of 1·0 in/sec were required then the necessary increase in amplitude can be found as follows:

$$A_p/g = 0·54 \times 5 \times v_m + 0·81 = 3·51$$

and the amplitude required is given by:

$$\frac{3·51 \times 32·2 \times 12}{(100\pi)^2} = 0·0137 \text{ in.}$$

Air-assisted feed tracks are often simply gravity feed tracks with air jets suitably placed to assist the transfer of the parts (Fig. 6.13). These devices are ideal for conditions where the gravity feed track alone will not quite meet the requirements. Whilst a well-designed air-assisted feed track can, under suitable conditions, feed the parts up an inclined track it is more usual for the track to slope downward.

For all types of feed track there are two important points which must be considered. For good space utilization a feed track should not be too long. Conversely, the feed track, besides acting as a transfer device, provides a buffer stock of parts which, if a blockage occurs, will allow the workhead to continue operating for a limited period. Ideally the feed track should be capable of holding enough parts to ensure that the workhead can continue to operate for a time sufficient to allow the blockage to be detected and cleared.

A further requirement for all feed tracks and indeed all parts feeders and workheads, is that in the event of a blockage, the parts are readily accessible. For this reason, feed tracks should be designed to allow easy access to all parts of the track.

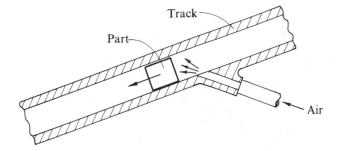

Figure 6.13. Air-assisted feed track.

6.3 Escapements

Many types of escapement have been developed and quite often, for a given part, there are several different types available which will perform the required function. Figure 6.14 shows two examples of probably the simplest type of escapement. Here, the parts are pulled from the feed track by the work carrier and the escapement itself consists of only a rocker arm or a spring blade.

Many escapements are not always recognized as such. For example, a rotary indexing table may be arranged to act as an escapement. This is shown in Fig. 6.15 where parts may be taken from either a vertical delivery feed track or a horizontal delivery feed track.

An advantage of the simple escapements illustrated in Figs. 6.14 and 6.15 is that they also act as parts placing mechanisms. The two escapements shown in Fig. 6.14 are somewhat unusual because the escapement is activated by the work carrier and part whereas with most escapements, the motion of the part is activated by the escapement which is in turn activated by some workhead function. This latter method is the most common in practice and escapements of this type may be subdivided into various categories as described below.

6.3.1 Ratchet Escapements

Two examples of ratchet escapements are shown in Fig. 6.16; the functions being performed are different in each case. The pawl is designed so that as its front finger lifts clear of the queue of parts, its back finger retains either the next part as shown in Fig. 6.16a

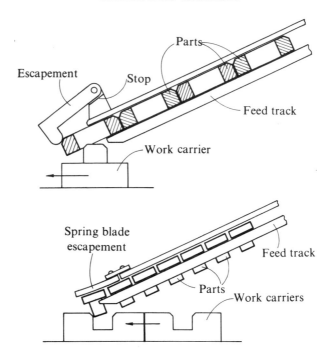

Figure 6.14. Escapements actuated by the work carrier.

or a part further up the queue as shown in Fig. 6.16b. Ratchet escapements operating on several feed tracks can be activated from a single mechanism. In mechanized assembly, the release of several parts from a single feed track is not often required but the release of one part from each of several feed tracks is often desirable. This can be achieved by a series of ratchet escapements of the type shown in Fig. 6.16a. As the escapement is activated, the front finger rotates, but without moving the part to be released. At position 2, the front finger is just about to release part A and the back finger has just engaged on part B. Further movement of the escapement allows part A to be released whilst the back finger moves in such a way that no motion is imparted to part B. On the return stroke of the escapement, part B is released by the back finger and retained by the front finger. Figure 6.16b shows a similar type of mechanism except that the remaining parts in that track move forward before being retained by the back finger. In these devices the back finger of the

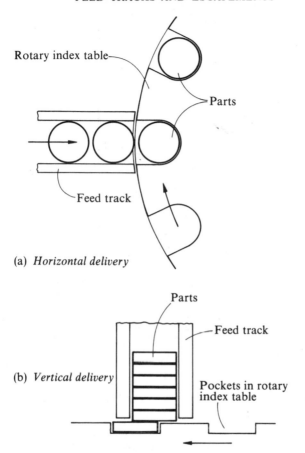

Rotary index table

Parts

Feed track

(a) *Horizontal delivery*

Parts

Feed track

(b) *Vertical delivery*

Pockets in rotary
index table

Figure 6.15. Feeding of parts onto rotary index table.

escapement should not produce motion of the parts opposite to the
direction of flow. If this tendency is present, either all the parts above
this point on the feed track will move backward and may subject the
escapement to heavy loads or the parts may lock and cause damage
to the escapement.

In the examples already shown, the motions of the front and back
fingers of the escapement are obtained by a rotary motion. The
fingers of a ratchet escapement may, however, be operated together
or independently by cams or solenoids giving a linear motion as
shown in Fig. 6.17.

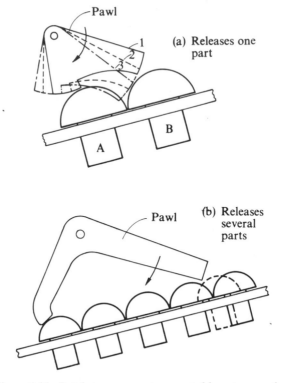

Figure 6.16. Ratchet escapements operated by rotary motion.

It is clear from all the above examples of ratchet escapements that the escapement can only be used to regulate the flow of parts which when arranged in single file have suitable gaps between their outer edges.

6.3.2 Slide Escapements

Five examples of slide escapements are shown in Figs. 6.18, 6.19 and 6.20. It can be seen from the figures that in the slide escapement one or more parts are removed from the feed chute by the action of a cross-slide and that applications of this type of device are restricted to parts which do not interlock with each other. The slide escapement is ideally suited to regulating the flow of spherical, cylindrical or plate-like parts and although in all the figures the feed track enters the escapement vertically, this, whilst desirable, is not necessary.

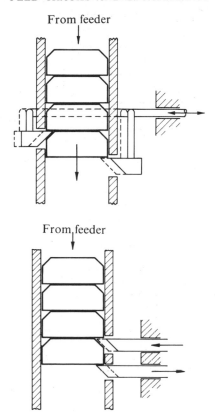

Figure 6.17. Ratchet escapements operated by linear motion.

As with the ratchet escapement, parts may be released either singly or in batches from one or a number of feed tracks by the action of a single actuating mechanism. However, a further alternative, not available with the ratchet escapement, is for parts fed from a single feed track to be equally divided between two delivery tracks as shown in Fig. 6.20a. This type of escapement is very useful where two identical parts are to be used in equal quantities and a parts feeder is available which will deliver at a sufficient rate to meet the total requirement. If it is necessary to feed parts from a single feed track into more than two delivery tracks a slide escapement of the type shown in Fig. 6.20b would be suitable. The figure shows three delivery tracks being fed from a single feed track and, as before, only one actuator is necessary.

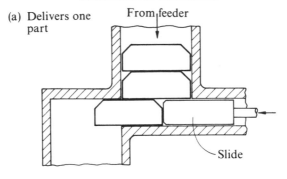

(a) Delivers one part

From feeder

Slide

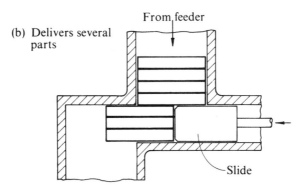

(b) Delivers several parts

From feeder

Slide

Figure 6.18. Slide escapements delivering into single feed chute.

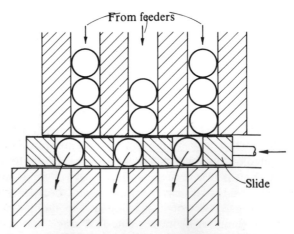

From feeders

Slide

Figure 6.19. Slide escapements operating several feed chutes.

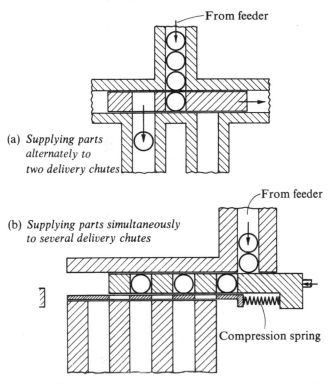

From feeder

(a) *Supplying parts
alternately to
two delivery chutes*

From feeder

(b) *Supplying parts simultaneously
to several delivery chutes*

Compression spring

*Figure 6.20. Slide escapements supplying two or more delivery chutes from a
single feed chute.*

6.3.3   Drum Escapements

Two types of drum escapement, usually referred to as drum-
spider escapements, are shown in Fig. 6.21 where in these cases the
drum is mounted vertically and the parts are either fed and delivered
side by side (Fig. 6.21a) or fed end to end and delivered side by side
(Fig. 6.21b). In the latter case the parts are fed horizontally to the
escapement. One advantage of the vertical drum escapement is that
a change in the direction of motion of the parts is easily accomplished. This can be very useful where the horizontal distance
between the parts feeder and the workhead is restricted to a value
which would necessitate very sharp curves in the feed track if an
alternative type of escapement were used. A further feature of the
drum-spider escapement is that on passing through the escapement,
the parts can be turned through a given angle.

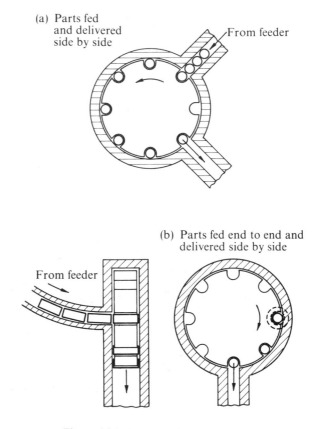

Figure 6.21. Drum-spider escapements.

Two other types of drum escapement, the star wheel and the worm, are shown in Fig. 6.22 where it can be seen that the direction of motion of the parts is unaffected by the escapement and it is necessary that the parts have a suitable gap between their outer edges when they are arranged in single file.

Drum escapements may be driven continuously or indexed but usually an indexing mechanism is preferable because difficulties may be encountered in attempting to synchronize a continuous drive to meet the requirements of the workhead. Of the six types of drum escapement described (Figs. 6.15, 6.21 and 6.22) the first four are effectively rotary slide escapements and the latter two rotary ratchet escapements.

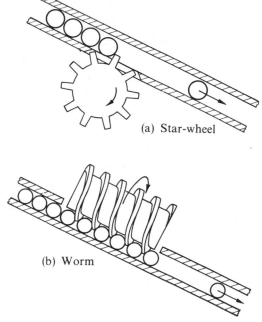

(a) Star-wheel

(b) Worm

Figure 6.22. Star-wheel and worm escapements.

6.3.4 Gate Escapements

The gate escapement is seldom used as a means of regulating the flow of parts to an automatic workhead on a mechanized assembly machine. Its main use is in providing an alternative path for parts and in this capacity it is often used for removing faulty parts from the main flow. However, one type of gate escapement, shown in Fig. 6.23, can be used to advantage on certain types of part when it is necessary to provide two equal outputs from a single feed track input. It is clear from the figure that whilst this device is usually referred to as an escapement it does not regulate the flow of parts and further escapements would be necessary on the delivery tracks to carry out this function.

6.3.5 Jaw Escapements

Jaw escapements are particularly useful in mechanized assembly applications where some forming process is necessary on the part after it has been placed in position in the assembly. Figure 6.24 shows

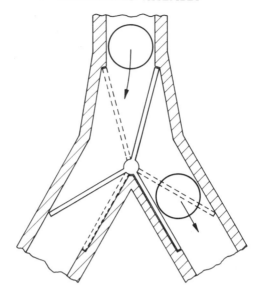

Figure 6.23. Gate escapement.

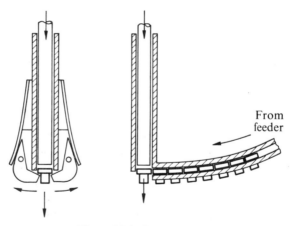

Figure 6.24. Jaw escapement.

an example of this type. The part is held by the jaws until the
actuator, in this case a punch, forces the part through the jaws. The
punch then performs the punching operation, returns, and allows
another part into the jaws. The device can, of course, be used purely
as an escapement.

6.4 Parts Placing Mechanisms

Two simple types of parts placing mechanism have already been described and illustrated in Figs. 6.14 and 6.15. In the first two examples the parts are taken from the feed track by the work carrier and in the other cases the parts are fed by gravity into pockets on a rotary index table. These special applications, however, can only be used for a very limited range of parts and by far the most widely used parts placing mechanism is a conventional gravity feed track working in conjunction with an escapement. This system of parts placing is probably the cheapest available but has certain limitations. Firstly, it may not be possible to place and fasten parts at the same position on the machine due to interference between the feed track and the workhead. This would necessitate a separate workstation for positioning the part which would result in an increase in the length of the machine. It then becomes necessary to retain the part in its correct orientation in the assembly during transfer. Secondly, if a close fit is required between the part and the assembly, the force due to gravity may not be sufficient to ensure that the part seats properly. Thirdly, if the part cannot be suitably chamfered, the gravity feed track may not give the precise location required. However, for placing of screws and rivets prior to fastening, which together form a large proportion of all parts placing requirements, and where the tool activates the escapement and applies the required force to make assembly possible, the gravity feed track is invariably used. An example of automatic screw placing and driving is shown in Fig. 6.25.

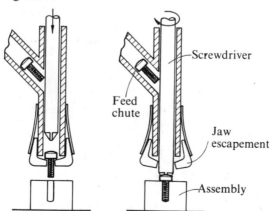

Figure 6.25. Parts placing mechanism for automatic screwdriver.

A further example of the assisted gravity feed type is shown in Fig. 6.24 where a part is being positioned in the assembly. With this device the feed track positions the part vertically above the assembly. The part is then guided into position in the assembly by a reciprocating guide rod. With these systems, it is common to fit the escapement at the point where the guide rod operates and to use the guide rod as the escapement activator. In some applications the part may be positioned above the assembly by means of a slide escapement and then guided into position using a guide rod. This system is commonly referred to as the 'push and guide' system of parts placing.

For situations where the placing mechanism has to be displaced from the work-station location, the 'pick and place' system is often used. The basic action of this system is shown in Figs. 6.26 and 6.27

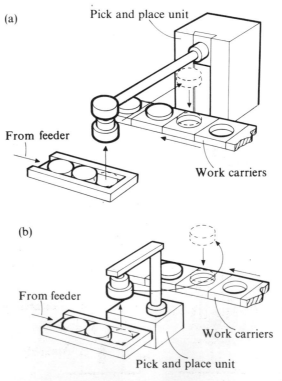

(a)

Pick and place unit

From feeder

Work carriers

(b)

From feeder

Work carriers

Pick and place unit

Figure 6.26. Pick and place units which lift and position the part vertically.

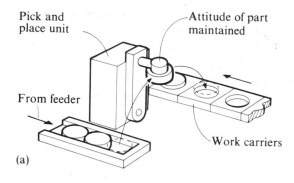

(a)

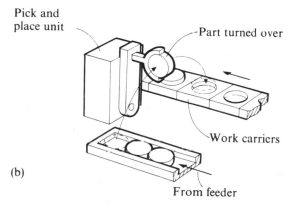

(b)

Figure 6.27. Pick and place units which move the part along the arc of a circle.

where it can be seen that the part is picked up from the feed track
by means of a mechanical, magnetic or vacuum hand, depending
on the particular application, placed in position in the assembly and
then released. The transfer arm then returns along the same path
to its initial position. Proprietary pick and place mechanisms
operate in a variety of ways. Some pick vertically, transfer along a
straight path horizontally and place vertically as shown in Fig. 6.26a.
Others pick vertically, transfer round the arc of a circle in a horizontal plane and place vertically as shown in Fig. 6.26b whilst a third
type picks and places by rotary motion of the transfer arm in a
vertical plane and throughout transfer the hand remains vertical
(Fig. 6.27a). Finally a variation of this latter type is where the pick-up
head is fixed to the arm and the part is turned over during the

operation (Fig. 6.27b). When operating correctly the first two examples can mate parts which have no chamfers and close assembly tolerances whereas the latter two examples, whilst being the simplest systems, will only operate when the length of vertical contact between the mating parts is small.

7.

Performance of Assembly Machines

Automatic assembly machines may be classified into two main groups according to the system used to transfer assemblies from workstation to workstation. The larger of the two groups includes those assembly machines which transfer all the work carriers simultaneously. These are known as indexing machines and a stoppage of any individual workhead causes the whole machine to stop. In the other group of machines, which are known as free-transfer assembly machines, the workheads are separated by buffer stocks of assemblies and transfer to and from these buffer stocks occurs when the particular workhead has completed its cycle of operations. Thus, with a free-transfer machine a fault or stoppage of a workhead will not necessarily prevent another workhead from operating because a limited supply of assemblies will usually be available in the adjacent buffer stocks.

One of the main problems in applying mechanization to the assembly process is the loss in production resulting from stoppages of automatic workheads when defective component parts are fed to the machine. With manual workstations on an assembly line, the operators are able to discard defective parts quickly and little loss of production occurs. However, a defective part fed to an automatic workhead can, on an indexing machine, cause a stoppage of the whole machine and production will cease until the fault is cleared. The resulting down-time can be very high with assembly machines having several automatic workheads. This can result in a serious loss in production and a consequent increase in the cost of assembly. The quality levels of the parts to be used in mechanized assembly must therefore be considered when an assembly machine is designed.

In the following a study is made of the effects of the quality levels of parts on the performance of assembly machines.

7.1   Indexing Machines

7.1.1   *Effect of Parts Quality on Down-time*

In the following analysis it will be assumed that an indexing machine having n automatic workheads and operating on a cycle time of t seconds is fed with parts having, on average, a ratio of defective parts to acceptable parts of x per cent. It will also be assumed that a proportion m of the defective parts will cause machine stoppages and further, that it will take an operator T seconds, on average, to locate the failure, remove the defective part and restart the machine.

With these assumptions, the total number of stoppages in producing N assemblies will be given by $mNxn/100$ and the time lost in production (down-time) due to these stoppages will be $mNxnT/100$. The machine time to assemble N assemblies is Nt seconds and thus the percentage down-time, D, on the machine is given by:

$$D = \frac{\text{down-time} \times 100}{\text{assembly time} + \text{down-time}}$$

$$= \frac{mxnNT}{Nt + mxnNT/100} = \frac{mxn}{0.01mxn + t/T} \text{ per cent} \qquad (7.1)$$

In practice, a reasonable value of the machine cycle time t, would be six seconds and experience shows that a typical value for the average time taken to clear a fault is 30 seconds. With these figures, the ratio t/T will be 0·2 and Fig. 7.1 shows the effect of variations in the mean quality level of the parts on the down-time for indexing machines with 5, 10, 15, and 20 automatic workheads. (It is assumed in this example that all defective parts will produce a stoppage of the machine and thus $m = 1$.)

For standard fasteners such as screws, which are often employed in assembly processes, an average value for x would be 2·0. In other words, for every 100 acceptable screws, there would be two defective ones. A higher quality level is generally available but with screws, for example, a reduction of x to 0·5 may double their price and seriously affect the cost of the final assembly. It will be seen later that a typical economic value for x is 1·0 and Fig. 7.1 shows that with this value the down-time on an assembly machine having 10 automatic workheads is 33 per cent of the total time available. These results show why it is rarely economic to use assembly machines having a large number of automatic workheads. They

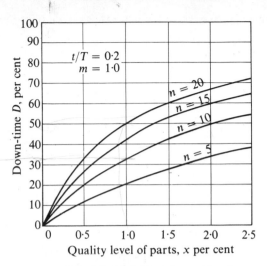

n = Number of automatic workheads
t = Machine cycle time, sec.
T = Time to correct machine fault, sec.
m = Proportion of defective parts causing
        machine stoppage

Figure 7.1. Effect of parts quality level on assembly machine down-time.

also illustrate why, in practice, it is common to allow for a total down-time of 50 per cent when considering the use of an indexing assembly machine.

7.1.2   Effect of Parts Quality on Production Rate

In the above example it was assumed that all the defective parts fed to the automatic workheads would stop the machine (i.e., $m = 1$ in eq. (7.1)). In practice, however, some of these defective parts would pass through the feeding devices and automatic workheads but would not be assembled correctly and would result in the production of an unacceptable assembly. In this case the effect of the defective part would be to cause down-time on the machine equal to only one machine cycle. The time taken to produce N assemblies, whether these are acceptable or not, is given by $(Nt + mNxnT/100)$ and if $m < 1$, only $(N - (1 - m)xnN/100)$ approximately of the assemblies produced will be acceptable. The production rate, P_a, of acceptable assemblies is therefore given by:

$$P_a = \frac{60(N - (1 - m)xnN/100)}{Nt + mNxnT/100} \text{ approximately}$$

$$= \frac{60(100 - (1 - m)xn)}{100t + mxnT} \text{ assemblies/min} \quad (7.2)$$

Taking typical values of $x = 1$, $t = 6$, $T = 30$ and $n = 10$, eq. (7.2) becomes:

$$P_a = \frac{18 + 2m}{2 + m} \quad (7.3)$$

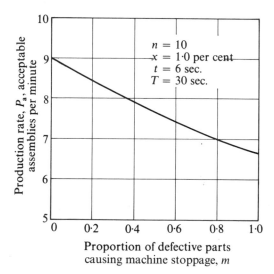

n = Number of automatic workheads
x = Ratio of defective to acceptable parts, per cent
t = Machine cycle time, sec.
T = Time to correct machine fault, sec.

Figure 7.2. Variation in assembly machine production rate with changes in the proportion of defective parts causing a machine fault.

Equation (7.3) is plotted in Fig. 7.2 to show the effect of m on P_a and it can be seen that for a maximum production rate of acceptable assemblies, m should be as small as possible. In other words, when designing the workheads for a mechanized assembly machine, and if a high production rate is required, it is preferable to allow a defective part to pass through the feeder and workhead and 'spoil' the assembly rather than allow it to stop the machine. However, in practical circumstances the cost of dealing with the unacceptable assemblies produced by the machine must be taken into account and this will be considered in the next chapter.

For the case where the defective parts always stop the machine, $m = 1$, and eq. (7.2) becomes:

$$P_a = \frac{6,000}{100t + xnT} \text{ assemblies/min} \tag{7.4}$$

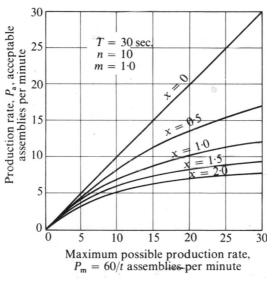

n = Number of automatic workheads
T = Time to correct machine fault, sec.
m = Proportion of defective parts causing
    machine stoppage

Figure 7.3. Effect of parts quality level on assembly machine production rate.

Figure 7.3 now shows how P_a is affected by changes in t for various values of x and for typical values of $T = 30$ and $n = 10$. For convenience, in the figure, the ratio $60/t$ is employed, which may be regarded as the maximum possible production rate, P_m, for a given cycle time. It can be seen that when x is small the production rate of acceptable assemblies, P_a, approaches the maximum possible production rate, P_m. However, in general, x will lie within the range 0·5 to 2·0 and under these circumstances it can be seen that for large values of P_m (short cycle times) P_a tends to become constant. Alternatively, it may be stated that as the cycle time is reduced for otherwise constant conditions, the percentage down-time increases and this results in a relatively small increase in the production rate. This explains why it is rarely practicable to have mechanized assembly machines working at very high speeds.

7.2 Free-transfer Machines

A free-transfer machine will always give a higher production rate than the equivalent indexing machine. This is because the buffer stocks of assemblies available between workheads will, for a limited time, allow the continued operation of the remaining workheads when one has stopped due to the feeding of a defective part. Provided the buffer stocks are sufficiently large, the stopped workhead can be restarted before the other workheads are affected. In this case the down-time on the machine will approach the down-time on the workhead which has the most stoppages. The following approximate analysis will show that, even with relatively small buffer stocks, the production rate of the machine can be considerably higher than that obtained with the equivalent indexing machine.

It will be assumed in the analysis that all the workheads on a free-transfer machine are working at the same cycle time of t seconds. Each workhead is fed with parts having the same quality level of x per cent (where x is the ratio of defective to acceptable parts), and between each pair of workstations is a buffer stock which will store b assemblies. Any workhead on a free-transfer assembly machine will be forced to stop under three different circumstances:

(a) If a defective part is fed to the workhead and prevents the completion of its cycle of operations. In this case it will be assumed that an interval of T seconds elapses before the fault is cleared and the workhead restarted;

(b) If the adjacent workhead 'up' the line has stopped and the supply of assemblies in the buffer stock between is exhausted;

(c) If the adjacent workhead 'down' the line has stopped and the buffer stock between is full.

If two adjacent workheads have a assemblies in the buffer stock between, then a fault in the first workhead will prevent the second from working after a time lag of at seconds. A fault in the second workhead will prevent the first from working after a time lag of $(b - a)t$ seconds. The analysis is based on the fact that over a long period the average down-time on each workhead must be the same. The assumption is made that no workhead will stop whilst another is stopped. The errors resulting from this assumption will become large when the quality level of the parts is poor (large x) and with a large number of automatic workheads (large n). However, specimen calculations show that these errors are negligible with practical values of x and n and that they will always produce an overestimate of the machine down-time.

7.2.1 *Performance of Five Station Machine.*

Considering the first workhead of a five station machine then, in producing N assemblies, $Nx/100$ stoppages will occur. If each fault takes T seconds to correct, the down-time on the first workhead due to its own stoppages is given by $NxT/100$. This same average down-time will apply to the second workhead but the first will only be prevented from working for a period of $Nx(T - (b - a_1)t)/100$ seconds, if a_1 is the average number of assemblies held in the buffer stock following the first workhead. Similarly, stoppages of the third workhead will only prevent the first from working for a period of $Nx(T - (2b - a_1 - a_2)t)/100$ seconds (a_2 is the average number of assemblies held in the buffer stock following the second workhead). Similar expressions can be derived for the effects of the fourth and fifth workheads.

Thus, it can be seen that the total down-time d_1 on the first workhead while the machine produces N assemblies is given by

$$100d_1/Nx = T + [T - (b - a_1)t] + [T - (2b - a_1 - a_2)t]$$
$$+ [T - (3b - a_1 - a_2 - a_3)t] + [T - (4b - a_1 - a_2 - a_3 - a_4)t]$$

$$(7.5)$$

It should be noted that if any term in square brackets is not positive it should be omitted.

Similar equations for the down-time on the remaining workheads may be derived and these are presented in Table 7.1.

If the condition is applied that the average down-time on all stations must be the same, then:

$$d_1 = d_2 = d_3 = d_4 = d_5 \qquad (7.6)$$

and the five equations in Table 7.1 may be solved simultaneously to give the values of a_1 to a_4 inclusive in terms of b. In the example, the appropriate values are:

$$a_1 = 4b/5, \; a_2 = 3b/5, \; a_3 = 2b/5, \text{ and } a_4 = b/5 \qquad (7.7)$$

Substituting these values in the equations for the down-time, d, on each workhead gives:

$$100d_1/Nx$$

$$= T + (T - bt/5) + (T - 3bt/5) + (T - 6bt/5) + (T - 10bt/5)$$

$$100d_2/Nx$$

$$= (T - 4bt/5) + T + (T - 2bt/5) + (T - 5bt/5) + (T - 9bt/5)$$

$$100d_3/Nx$$

$$= (T - 7bt/5) + (T - 3bt/5) + T + (T - 3bt/5) + (T - 7bt/5)$$

$$100d_4/Nx$$

$$= (T - 9bt/5) + (T - 5bt/5) + (T - 2bt/5) + T + (T - 4bt/5)$$

$$100d_5/Nx$$

$$= (T - 10bt/5) + (T - 6bt/5) + (T - 3bt/5) + (T - bt/5) + T$$

$$(7.8)$$

It is necessary at this stage to know the relative values of T and t. If, for example, the ratio $T/t = 5$, then the above solution only applies for $b \leqslant 2$, otherwise some of the bracketed terms in eqs. (7.8) will become negative and must be omitted in the original equations in Table 7.1. For $b \leqslant 2$ the down-time d for the machine is now given from any eq. (7.8):

$$\frac{100d}{tNx} = 25 - 4b \qquad (7.9)$$

The percentage down-time, D, on the machine may now be obtained as follows:

$$D = \frac{\text{down-time} \times 100}{\text{assembly time} + \text{down-time}} = \frac{100d}{Nt + d} \text{ per cent} \qquad (7.10)$$

and substitution of d from eq. (7.9) gives:

$$D = \frac{(25 - 4b)x}{1 + 0 \cdot 01(25 - 4b)x} \text{ per cent} \qquad (7.11)$$

TABLE 7.1

General Equations for the Down-time, d, at Each Station of a Five Station Assembly Machine

Workhead	Down-time due to First workhead	Second workhead	Third workhead	Fourth workhead	Fifth workhead
First, $\dfrac{100d_1}{Nx} =$	T	$+[T-(b-a_1)t]$	$+[T-(2b-a_1-a_2)t]$	$+[T-(3b-a_1-a_2-a_3)t]$	$+[T-(4b-a_1-a_2-a_3-a_4)t]$
Second, $\dfrac{100d_2}{Nx} =$	$[T-a_1t]$	$+T$	$+[T-(b-a_2)t]$	$+[T-(2b-a_2-a_3)t]$	$+[T-(3b-a_2-a_3-a_4)t]$
Third, $\dfrac{100d_3}{Nx} =$	$[T-(a_1+a_2)t]$	$+[T-a_2t]$	$+T$	$+[T-(b-a_3)t]$	$+[T-(2b-a_3-a_4)t]$
Fourth, $\dfrac{100d_4}{Nx} =$	$[T-(a_1+a_2+a_3)t]$	$+[T-(a_2+a_3)t]$	$+[T-a_3t]$	$+T$	$+[T-(b-a_4)t]$
Fifth, $\dfrac{100d_5}{Nx} =$	$[T-(a_1+a_2+a_3+a_4)t]$	$+[T-(a_2+a_3+a_4)t]$	$+[T-(a_3+a_4)t]$	$+[T-a_4t]$	$+T$

TABLE 7.2

Effect of Buffer Stock Size, b, on Average Number of Assemblies, a, in Each Buffer Stock

Values of b	Omit terms in equations (Table 7.1)					Values of a			
	d_1	d_2	d_3	d_4	d_5	$\dfrac{a_1}{b}$	$\dfrac{a_2}{b}$	$\dfrac{a_3}{b}$	$\dfrac{a_4}{b}$
0, 1, 2	—	—	—	—	—	4/5	3/5	2/5	1/5
3	5	5	—	1	1	3/4	7/12	5/12	1/4
4	4, 5	5	1, 5	1	1, 2	3/4	1/2	1/2	1/4
5, 6	4, 5	4, 5	1, 5	1, 2	1, 2	2/3	5/9	4/9	1/3
7	3, 4, 5	4, 5	1, 5	1, 2	1, 2, 3	22/35	19/35	16/35	13/35
8	3, 4, 5	4, 5	1, 5	1, 2	1, 2, 3	23/40	21/40	19/40	17/40
9	3, 4, 5	4, 5	1, 5	1, 2	1, 2, 3	24/45	23/45	22/45	21/45
10 →	2, 3, 4, 5	1, 3, 4, 5	1, 2, 4, 5	1, 2, 3, 5	1, 2, 3, 4	1/2	1/2	1/2	1/2

For $b \geqslant 3$ and with $T/t = 5$ some of the bracketed terms in eqs. (7.8) will become zero or negative and the corresponding terms in the equations in Table 7.1 must therefore be omitted. In this case, new values of a_1 to a_4 will be obtained and the magnitudes of the bracketed terms in the revised eqs. (7.8) must be re-examined.

Table 7.2 shows, for the ratio $T/t = 5$ and for increasing values of b, which terms in the original equations become zero or negative and gives the corresponding values of a_1 to a_4.

Having determined the values of a_1 to a_4 for each value of b, the percentage down-time on the machine may be calculated in the manner described above.

In general for $0 \leqslant b \leqslant 10$, the machine down-time, d may be expressed as:

$$d = \frac{KNxt}{100} \tag{7.12}$$

where K is a factor which depends, for a given value of T/t, on the value of b. Table 7.3 gives the values of K for various values of b when $T/t = 5$.

TABLE 7.3

Relationship Between Buffer Stock Size, b and the Factor K

b	K
0	25·0
2	17·0
4	11·0
6	8·33
8	6·6
10	5·0

The percentage down-time, D, is now given by:

$$D = \frac{100d}{Nt + d} = \frac{Kx}{1 + 0·01Kx} \text{ per cent} \tag{7.13}$$

For $b \geqslant 10$ all bracketed terms are omitted from the equations in Table 7.1 and the equation for the down-time on each workhead becomes

$$\frac{100d}{Nx} = T \tag{7.14}$$

The percentage down-time on the machine then becomes equal to the percentage down-time on an individual workhead and thus for $b \geqslant 10$

$$D = \frac{5x}{1 + 0{\cdot}05x} \qquad\qquad (7.15)$$

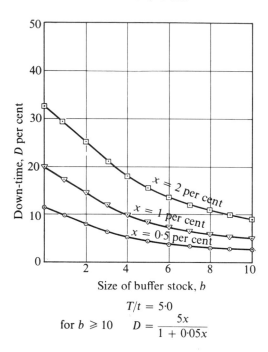

$T/t = 5{\cdot}0$

for $b \geqslant 10$ $D = \dfrac{5x}{1 + 0{\cdot}05x}$

Figure 7.4. Effect of buffer stock size on down-time for a five station free-transfer assembly machine.

Figure 7.4 shows how the percentage down-time is affected by the size of the buffer stocks for values of $x = 0{\cdot}5$, $1{\cdot}0$, and $2{\cdot}0$. It can be seen that significant improvements in performance can be obtained with only small buffer stocks and that with large buffer stocks the machine down-time approaches one-fifth of the down-time on an equivalent indexing machine (given by $b = 0$).

7.2.2   Performance of Free-transfer Machines when the Quality Levels of the Parts vary from Station to Station.

For simplicity in the above analysis, it was assumed that the quality level of the parts was identical for each workhead (i.e.,

$x_1 = x_2 = x_3 = x_4 = x_5$). In a practical situation this will not generally be the case but the procedure described above may still be employed to predict machine performance. It is clear, however, that unlike the indexing machine, the down-time on a free-transfer machine may be affected by the relative positions of the workheads when the quality levels of the parts vary from workhead to workhead. It can be argued that, in this case, the workheads with the worst quality levels (large x) should be placed as near to either end of the machine as possible where they will influence a minimum number of the remaining workheads. This is now illustrated by a simple example:

It will be assumed that a three station in-line free-transfer assembly machine has buffer stocks between stations capable of holding four assemblies each. The parts fed to the workheads have quality levels x_1, x_2, and x_3 of 1·0, 2·0, and 1·0 per cent defectives respectively. Assuming that $T/t = 5$, the down-time for this arrangement will be compared with that obtained when the workhead dealing with parts having 2 per cent defectives is placed at one end of the machine. The appropriate equations for the down-time at each workhead are:

$$\left.\begin{aligned} &100d_1/N \\ &= x_1 T + x_2[T - (b - a_1)t] + x_3[T - (2b - a_1 - a_2)t] \\ &100d_2/N \\ &= x_1[T - a_1 t] + x_2 T + x_3[T - (b - a_2)t] \\ &100d_3/N \\ &= x_1[T - (a_1 + a_2)t] + x_2[T - a_2 t] + x_3 T \end{aligned}\right\} \quad (7.16)$$

(a) Writing $x_1 = x_3 = 1·0$ and $x_2 = 2·0$ in eqs. (7.16) and since $d_1 = d_2 = d_3$, the values of a_1 and a_2 may be found. Thus:

$$a_1 = 3b/4 \quad \text{and} \quad a_2 = b/4$$

With these values and since $T/t = 5$, none of the terms in eqs. (7.16) should be omitted and thus from any eq. (7.16), $d = 14Nt/100$. Hence the percentage down-time, D, is given by:

$$D = \frac{14Nt}{14Nt/100 + Nt} = 12·3 \text{ per cent}$$

(b) Writing $x_1 = x_2 = 1·0$ and $x_3 = 2·0$ in eqs. (7.16), the values of a_1 and a_2 become:

$$a_1 = 3b/4 \quad \text{and} \quad a_2 = b/2$$

Again, none of the terms in eqs. (7.16) should be omitted and thus it is found that $d = 13Nt/100$. Hence:

$$D = \frac{13Nt}{13Nt/100 + Nt} = 11 \cdot 5 \text{ per cent}$$

The results of this example indicate that workheads dealing with parts having poor quality should be situated as near the end of the machine as possible.

It should be pointed out that the method of analysis for free-transfer machines presented in this chapter is only approximate and assumes that the breakdowns due to defective parts will not occur in quick succession on the same workhead. Experimental work on an analogue of a free-transfer machine[1] has shown that the analysis gives a good approximation to the true performance of a machine when $b \leqslant T/t$.

It should also be noted that the analysis only applies to a machine where relatively large buffer stocks of empty work carriers are held in the return conveyor between the last and the first workheads. If this were not the case then the basic equations would need modification to allow for a direct influence of breakdowns at the last station on the performance of the first, and vice versa.

Reference

1. HUNTER, G. Unpublished Work. Royal College of Advanced Technology, Salford.

8.

Economics of Assembly Machines

It has already been shown that the production rate of an assembly machine is seriously affected by the quality levels of the various component parts fed to it. In this chapter analyses will be made of the economics of the two main types of assembly machine. One of the main problems studied will be whether the savings in assembly costs due to the improvement in production obtained by using parts of higher quality can offset the higher cost of the parts.

8.1 Effect of Parts Quality on the Cost of Assembly by Indexing Machines

The total cost, C_t, of each acceptable assembly produced on an assembly machine is given by the sum of the costs of the individual parts $C_1 + C_2 + C_3 + \ldots C_n$ and the cost, C_a, of operating the machine for the average time taken to produce one acceptable assembly. Thus:

$$C_t = C_a + C_1 + C_2 + C_3 + \ldots C_n$$
$$= M_t/P_a + C_1 + C_2 + C_3 + \ldots C_n \qquad (8.1)$$

where M_t is the total cost of operating the machine for one minute and includes operators' wages, overhead charges, actual operating costs, machine depreciation, and the cost of dealing with the unacceptable assemblies produced. P_a is the production rate of acceptable assemblies and may be obtained from eq. (7.2).

In estimating M_t it will be assumed that a machine stoppage caused by a defective part will be cleared by one of the operators employed on the machine and that no extra cost will be entailed other than that due to machine down-time. Further, it will be assumed that if a defective part passes through the workhead and 'spoils' an assembly it will take an extra operator T_c minutes to

137

dismantle the assembly and replace the 'non-defective' parts in the appropriate feeding devices.

Thus the total operating cost M_t is given by:

$$M_t = M + P_u T_c W \qquad (8.2)$$

where M is the cost of operating the machine for one minute if only acceptable assemblies are produced (shillings/min) and W is the operator's rate including overheads (shillings/min).

P_u is the production rate of unacceptable assemblies and is given by:

$$P_u = \frac{60(1 - m)xn}{100t + mxnT} \qquad (8.3)$$

Substitution of eq. (8.3) in eq. (8.2) gives:

$$M_t = M + \frac{60(1 - m)xnT_c W}{100t + mxnT} \qquad (8.4)$$

In estimating the cost, C, of an individual component part, it will be assumed that this can be broken down into: (a) the basic cost of the part irrespective of quality level; (b) a cost which is inversely proportional to x and which will therefore increase as the quality level is increased. Thus the cost of each part may be expressed as follows:

$$C = A_b + B/x \qquad (8.5)$$

B is a measure of the increase in cost due to increased quality level and for the purposes of the present analysis this will be assumed constant regardless of the basic cost, A_b, of the parts.

If eqs. (8.4) and (8.5) are now substituted in eq. (8.1) the total cost, C_t, of each acceptable assembly becomes, after re-arrangement:

$$C_t = \frac{M(100t + mxnT)/60 + (1 - m)xnT_c W}{100 - (1 - m)xn} + \sum A_b + nB/x \qquad (8.6)$$

Equation (8.6) shows that the total cost of an assembly can be broken down as follows:

(a) A cost which will decrease as x is reduced;
(b) A cost which is constant;
(c) A cost which will increase as x is reduced.

It follows that for a given situation an optimum value of x may exist which will give minimum cost of assembly. For the moment, the optimum value of x will be considered for the case where $m = 1$ (i.e., where all defective parts cause a stoppage of the machine).

With $m = 1$, eq. (8.6) becomes:

$$C_t = M(100t + xnT)/6{,}000 + \sum A_b + nB/x \qquad (8.7)$$

Equation (8.7) is now differentiated with respect to x and equated to zero yielding the following expression for the optimum value of x giving minimum cost of assembly:

$$x_{opt} = 10(60B/MT)^{\frac{1}{2}} \qquad (8.8)$$

It is interesting to note that for a given assembly machine, where M and B are constants, the optimum quality level of the parts used is dependent only on the time taken to clear a defective part from a workhead.

Figure 8.1 shows how the cost of a common type of screw increases as the quality level is improved. In this case $A_b = B = 0{\cdot}0167$

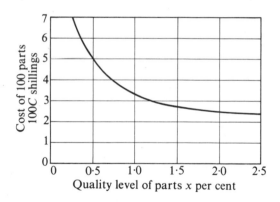

Figure 8.1. Typical relationship between parts quality level and cost.

shillings per screw. If typical values of $M = 3$ shillings per minute and $T = 30$ sec are now substituted in eq. (8.8) the corresponding optimum value of x is approximately 1 per cent. Equation (8.8) may now be substituted in eq. (8.7) to give an expression for the minimum cost of assembly:

$$C_t(\text{min}) = Mt/60 + 2n(MBT/60)^{\frac{1}{2}}/10 + \sum A_b \qquad (8.9)$$

With $t = 6$ sec and $n = 10$, the cost of assembling each set of parts would be $0{\cdot}62$ shillings. Half of this cost would be attributable to the assembly operation itself and the other half attributable to the increased cost of higher quality parts and the cost of machine down-time (in this case 33 per cent). Figure 8.2 shows how these individual costs would vary as the quality level x varies, using the figures quoted in the example above. In this case, if parts having 2 per cent defective were to be used instead of the optimum value of 1 per cent, the cost of assembly would increase by approximately 11 per cent. This is a variation of 0·066 shillings per assembly and with an average production rate of 6·7 assemblies per minute (calculated from eq. (7.2)), represents an extra expense of approximately 160 shillings for a six-hour shift.

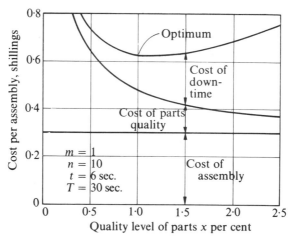

Figure 8.2. Effect of parts quality level on assembly costs.

In the above analysis it was assumed that all the defective parts would stop the machine. If, instead, it were possible to allow these parts to pass through the automatic devices and 'spoil' the assemblies, the cost of assembly could be obtained by writing $m = 0$ in eq. (8.6). Thus:

$$C_t = \frac{M(100t)/60 + xnT_cW}{100 - xn} + \sum A_b + nB/x \qquad (8.10)$$

Again an optimum value of x arises and this is found, by differentiation of eq. (8.10) to be:

$$x_{opt} = 100/[n + (100T_cW/B + 5Mt/3B)^{\frac{1}{2}}] \qquad (8.11)$$

Taking $W = 0·2$ shillings per minute and $T_c = 1$ min and the remaining figures as before, x is found to be approximately 1·5 per cent. From eq. (8.10) the minimum cost of assembly is 0·50 shillings which represents a saving of 19 per cent on the cost of assembly compared with the previous example.

It is possible to draw two main conclusions from the above work. First, for the situation analysed it would be preferable to allow a defective part to pass through the workhead and 'spoil' the assembly rather than allow it to stop the machine. This would not only increase the production rate of acceptable assemblies but would also reduce the cost of assembly. Second, an optimum quality level of parts always exists which will give minimum cost of assembly.

8.2   Gradual Mechanization of an Indexing Assembly Machine

In practice, mechanization of an operator assembly line is sometimes carried out step by step. This means that individual assembly operators are gradually replaced by automatic workheads. The simplest operations are usually mechanized first, and the more complicated operations, being the more expensive to mechanize, are left until later.

To study this problem, the effect on assembly costs of the gradual mechanization of an operator assembly line will be analysed and, in order to illustrate the trends clearly it will be assumed throughout that all defective parts will cause a stoppage of the machine (i.e., $m = 1$).

The analysis will deal with the assembly of a product which requires q assembly operations. At each workstation on the assembly machine, only one operation is performed at a constant cycle time, t seconds. Thus, if n represents the number of automatic workheads, the number of operators employed on the machine will be given by $(q - n)$. It will be assumed that the rate for each operator including overheads, is W shillings/min, that the depreciation rate per workstation of the basic transfer device is C_T shillings/min, and that the depreciation rate of an automatic workhead (which replaces one operator) is C_A shillings/min.

In this case, the total cost M of operating the machine is given by:

$$M = W(q - n) + qC_T + nC_A \text{ shillings/min} \qquad (8.12)$$

Equation (8.12) may now be substituted in eq. (8.7) to give the cost, C_t, per acceptable assembly produced on the machine. Thus:

$$C_t = [W(q - n) + qC_T + nC_A](100t + xnT)/6{,}000 + \sum A_b + nB/x \qquad (8.13)$$

The optimum quality level x_{opt} of the parts is given by substitution of eq. (8.12) in eq. (8.8). Thus:

$$x_{opt} = 10\{60B/[W(q - n) + qC_T + nC_A]T\}^{\frac{1}{2}} \qquad (8.14)$$

In order to observe how the minimum cost of assembly varies as n is gradually increased, the following typical values of the various constants are substituted in eqs. (8.13) and (8.14):

$$C_T = 0.15, \quad C_A = 0.06, \quad W = 0.2, \quad t = 6, \quad T = 30, \quad T_c = 1.0$$

$$\text{and} \quad B = 0.0167$$

Figure 8.3 shows, for a variety of conditions, how the minimum cost of assembly varies as an operator assembly line is mechanized step by step, i.e., as n is increased until $n = q$, when the line becomes

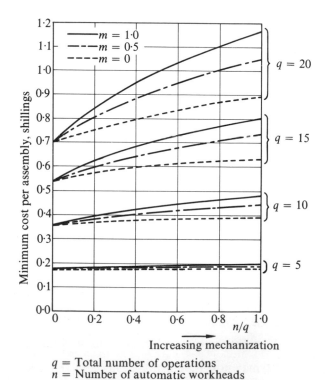

q = Total number of operations
n = Number of automatic workheads
m = Proportion of defective parts causing
machine stoppage

Figure 8.3. Effect of increasing mechanization on assembly costs.

fully automatic. Figure 8.4 shows, for typical conditions, how the production rate varies as n is increased. It can be seen from these results that with the values of the constants chosen, mechanization increases the minimum cost per assembly and reduces the production rate. This increase in cost was obtained even though the depreciation

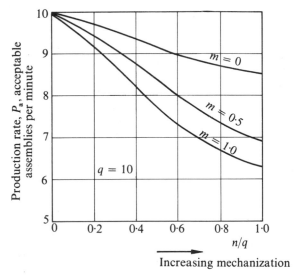

q = Total number of operations
n = Number of automatic workheads
m = Proportion of defective parts causing
    machine stoppage

Figure 8.4. Effect of increasing mechanization on production rate.

rate of an automatic workhead was assumed to be only one-third of the rate for one operator. This result is more clearly seen in the graph presented in Fig. 8.5 which gives a breakdown of the assembly costs for typical conditions. It can be seen that, as the assembly line becomes increasingly mechanized:

(a) The operating cost per assembly for the basic transfer device increases gradually. This is due to the reduced production rate caused by machine stoppages;

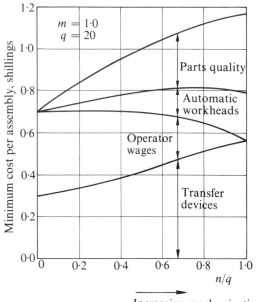

Increasing mechanization

q = Total number of operations
n = Number of automatic workheads
m = Proportion of defective parts causing
machine stoppage

Figure 8.5. Breakdown of assembly costs and the effect of increasing mechanization.

(b) The operator costs per assembly reduce gradually to zero. This reduction is only small at low values of n, again because of the reduced production rate;

(c) The cost per assembly for the automatic workheads increases gradually and this relatively small added cost is sufficient to give an increase in assembly cost as the assembly line becomes increasingly mechanized;

(d) Finally, the increased cost of higher quality parts for the automatic workheads is sufficient to produce a rapidly increasing total cost of assembly as the assembly line becomes increasingly mechanized. This increase is mainly a result of the increased number of automatic heads which require higher quality parts than the operator work stations. The optimum quality level for the automatic heads, when $q = 20$, only varied from $x = 0.7$ when $n/q = 0.2$ to $x = 0.88$ when $n/q = 1.0$.

In the above analysis, it was assumed that an assembly line working on a fixed cycle time is mechanized step by step by gradually replacing the operators with automatic workheads. The results of the example quoted above show that this process can, under typical conditions, produce a rapidly increasing cost of assembly and a significantly reduced production rate. This indicates that in practice it will be necessary to give very careful consideration to the economics of the gradual mechanization of operator assembly lines.

With an indexing assembly machine, the machine cycle time is determined by the slowest operation which in general will be the slowest manual operation. However, with a free-transfer machine the cycle time may be allowed to vary from station to station. In this case the cycle time of the automatic workheads could be shorter than the time for the manual operations so that when a breakdown occurs due to a defective part there will generally be a sufficient 'backlog' of work at the next 'slow' operator station to prevent the stoppage of the whole line. In this case, with increasing mechanization, the production rate may not fall off as rapidly as with an indexing machine. It follows that the total cost of assembly may then reduce with increasing mechanization.

It has already been shown in chapter 7 that a free-transfer machine will always give a higher production rate than the equivalent indexing machine. In the following, the economics of a free-transfer machine will be studied and the assembly costs compared with those for an equivalent indexing machine.

8.3   Economics of a Five Station Free-transfer Machine

When considering the economics of a free-transfer machine, the extra cost of providing the buffer stocks has to be taken into account.

It will be assumed that the total cost, M_t, of operating the machine, will include the cost, C_A, of each automatic workhead, the cost, C_T, of each section of the transfer device and the work carrier, the cost, C_B, of each work carrier in the buffer stock and the associated provision for transfer, the operating costs and overhead charges, M, for the machine, and the total cost, W_T, of all operators employed on the machine. Thus:

$$M_t = n(C_A + C_T + bC_B) + M + W_T \qquad (8.15)$$

where b = number of work carriers per buffer stock.

The mean production rate, P_a will be given by

$$P_a = 60N/(Nt + d) \qquad (8.16)$$

where t = machine cycle time, sec and d = machine down-time in producing N assemblies, sec.

In the analysis presented in chapter 7 for estimating the effect of the size of the buffer stocks on a free-transfer assembly machine it was shown that the machine down-time, d in producing N assemblies could be expressed by:

$$d = KNxt/100 \qquad (8.17)$$

where K is a factor depending on the size of the buffer stock. Substituting eqs. (8.15), (8.16), (8.5), and (8.17) in eq. (8.1) gives the following expression for the total assembly cost. Thus:

$$C_t = t(nC_A + nC_T + nbC_B + M + W_T)(100 + Kx)/6{,}000$$
$$+ \sum A_b + nB/x \qquad (8.18)$$

By differentiating eq. (8.18) with respect to x and equating to zero, the optimum parts quality level, x_{opt}, for minimum cost is obtained. Thus:

$$x_{opt} = 10[60B/Kt(C_A + C_T + bC_B + M/n + W_T/n)]^{\frac{1}{2}} \qquad (8.19)$$

Typical values of the parameters in eq. (8.19) are as follows:

$C_A = 0.06,\quad C_T = 0.15,\quad C_B = 0.003,\quad M = 0.01,\quad W_T = 0.2,$
$B = 0.0167,\ t = 6,$ and $n = 5.$

Values of K for a five station free-transfer machine, when $T/t = 5$, are given in Table 7.3.

In estimating the operator costs, W_T, it was assumed that only one operator would be required to correct faults on the machine. Using these figures and eq. (8.19), the values of x_{opt} corresponding to various sizes of buffer stock can be found and these are presented in Table 8.1.

In practice, it is not possible to obtain parts with a wide range of quality levels and with many proprietary fasteners, for example, there would be a guaranteed minimum quality level. Thus, quality levels indicating more than 2 per cent defectives, such as those in Table 8.1, may be unrealistic since no corresponding reduction in cost would be obtainable. For this reason, a quality level of 2 per cent will be assumed throughout the present analysis.

TABLE 8.1

Effect of Buffer Stock Size, b, on the
Optimum Quality Level of Parts, x_{opt}

b	x_{opt}
0	1·63
2	1·93
4	2·38
6	2·74
8	3·06
10	3·44

When considering the economics of mechanized assembly, it is usual to compare the assembly costs with those of operator assembly. If, in the present example, the automatic workheads were replaced by five operators and the buffer stocks eliminated, the total cost of operator assembly, C_{to}, would be given by:

$$C_{to} = (t/60)[5(C_T + W) + M]/60 + \sum A_b + 5B/2 \qquad (8.20)$$

In order to compare the relative costs of automatic and operator assembly, eq. (8.18), with $W_T = W$, $x = 2$, and $n = 5$, is now subtracted from eq. (8.20). Thus:

$$C_{to} - C_t = (t/60)[W(4 - K/50) - C_A(5 + K/10) - C_T K/10$$
$$- bC_B(5 + K/10) - MK/50] \qquad (8.21)$$

Substituting the values of t, W, C_A, C_T, C_B, and M specified above and values of K from Table 7.3 will now give the savings to be obtained with mechanized assembly. The results are presented in Fig. 8.6 where it can be seen that the machine with no buffer stocks is uneconomic compared with operator assembly and that as larger buffer stocks are provided the cost of assembly reduces. For a buffer stock of two at each station, the machine breaks even with the manual operator line and with larger buffer stocks, the cost of assembly is less than the cost of operator assembly. It is interesting to note that savings of as much as 1·5 shillings per 100 assemblies are possible with buffer stocks of only four.

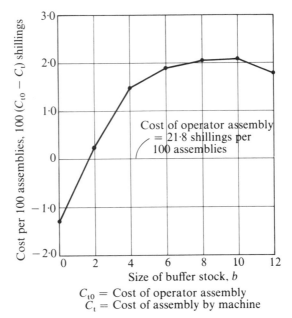

C_{t0} = Cost of operator assembly
C_t = Cost of assembly by machine

Figure 8.6. Effect of buffer stock size on assembly costs for a five station free-transfer machine.

Substitution of eq. (8.17) in eq. (8.16), gives the production rate, P_a. Thus:

$$P_a = 6{,}000/t(100 + Kx) \text{ assemblies/min} \qquad (8.22)$$

Figure 8.7 shows how the production rate increases as the buffer stock is increased and since, with the approximate analysis the down-time cannot be reduced with buffer stocks larger than 10, the production rate theoretically becomes constant for all values of b greater than 10.

Clearly, the results obtained in the examples given in this chapter depended on the values of the various constants used in the expressions. It should not be assumed therefore that an indexing machine will always give higher assembly costs than a free-transfer machine. The purpose of these analyses and examples is not to state a case for one particular type of machine but to illustrate some of the possible pitfalls of mechanized assembly. In a particular situation it should be possible to substitute estimated values of the various constants in the appropriate expressions and hence obtain an assessment of the economics of a given proposal.

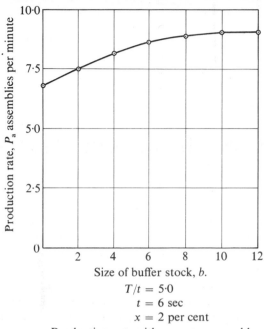

$$T/t = 5{\cdot}0$$
$$t = 6 \text{ sec}$$
$$x = 2 \text{ per cent}$$

Production rate with operator assembly
= 10 assemblies/min.

Figure 8.7. Effect of buffer stock size on the production rate of a five station free-transfer assembly machine.

9.

Design for Mechanized Assembly

Experience shows that it is difficult to make large savings in cost by the introduction of mechanized assembly in the manufacture of an existing product. In those cases where large savings are claimed, examination will show that often the savings are really due to changes in the design of the product necessitated by the introduction of the new process. It can probably be stated that in most of these instances even greater savings would be made if the new product were to be assembled manually. Undoubtedly, the greatest cost savings are to be made by careful consideration of the design of the product and its individual component parts.

When a product is designed, consideration is generally given to the ease of manufacture of its individual parts and the function and appearance of the final product. Whilst for obvious reasons it must be possible to assemble the product, little thought is usually given to those aspects of design which will facilitate assembly of the parts and great reliance is often placed on the dexterity of the assembly operators. An operator is able to select, inspect, orient, transfer, place, and assemble the most complicated parts relatively easily but many of these operations are difficult, if not impossible, to duplicate on a machine. Thus, one of the first steps in the introduction of mechanization in the assembly process is to reconsider the design of the product so that the individual assembly operations become sufficiently simple for a machine to perform.

The subject of design for mechanized assembly can be conveniently divided into two sections: product design for ease of assembly; design of parts for feeding and orienting.

9.1 Product Design for Ease of Assembly

The most obvious way in which the assembly process can be facilitated at the design stage is by reducing the number of different parts to a minimum. An example of this is given by Iredale[1] and shown in Fig. 9.1. Here the original design consisted of 13 parts and required many difficult operations to assemble. The new design reduced the product to two parts requiring only one simple operation

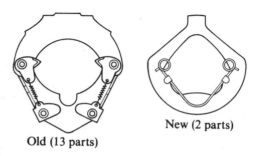

New (2 parts)

Old (13 parts)

Figure 9.1. Reduction of parts to save assembly costs. (After Iredale[1].)

to assemble. Clearly, great savings in production cost would have been brought about by this reconsideration of the design of the product. Further examples of product simplification for mechanized assembly are given in Fig. 9.2.

It is sometimes possible to simplify a product by employing one of the new processes which enable complex parts to be produced. These parts can sometimes replace complete sub-assemblies and hence eliminate many assembly operations. The new forming and casting operations are examples of processes which may help in this respect and in particular, precision die casting is being increasingly applied.

One important factor may arise during the re-design of a product. For instance it might be suggested in a particular situation that a screw, nut, and washer might be replaced by a rivet, or alternatively, that the parts might be joined by welding or by the use of adhesives. This would eliminate at least two assembly operations but would result in a product which would be more difficult to repair. This illustrates a common trend where the introduction of mechanization may result in a cheaper product but one which is quite uneconomical to repair. In the future, consumers will probably become more accustomed to the idea of replacing the complete product or a major sub-assembly in the event of a failure.

Apart from product simplification, great improvements can often be made by the introduction of guides and tapers which directly facilitate assembly. Examples of this are given by Baldwin[2] and

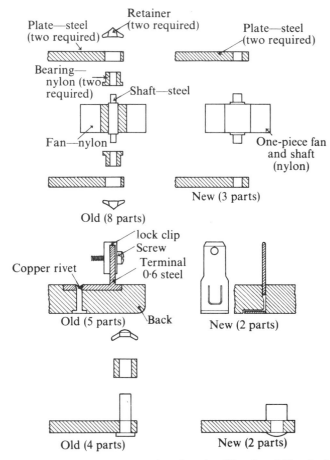

Figure 9.2. Further examples of product simplification. (After Iredale[1].)

Tipping[3] in Figs. 9.3 and 9.4. In both these examples sharp corners are removed so that the part to be assembled is guided into its correct position during assembly.

Further examples in this category can be found in the type of screw used in mechanized assembly. Those screws which tend to centralize themselves in the hole will give the best results in mechanized assembly and Tipping[3] summarizes and grades the designs of screw point available as follows (Fig. 9.5):

(a) Rolled thread point—very poor location; will not centralize without positive control on the outside diameter of the screw;

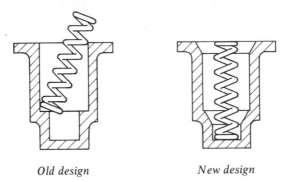

Old design   New design

Figure 9.3. Re-design of product for ease of assembly. (After Baldwin[2].)

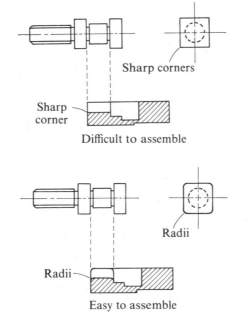

Sharp corners

Sharp corner

Difficult to assemble

Radii

Radii

Easy to assemble

Figure 9.4. Re-design to assist assembly. (After Tipping[3].)

(b) Header point—only slightly better than (a) if of correct shape;
(c) Chamfer point—reasonable to locate;
(d) Dog point—reasonable to locate;
(e) Cone point—very good to locate;
(f) Oval point—very good to locate.

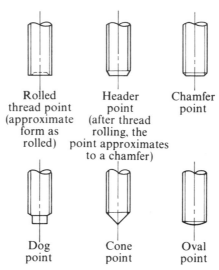

Rolled
thread point
(approximate
form as
rolled)

Header
point
(after thread
rolling, the
point approximates
to a chamfer)

Chamfer
point

Dog
point

Cone
point

Oval
point

Figure 9.5. Various forms of screw point.

Tipping recommends that only the cone and oval point screws be used in mechanized assembly.

Another factor to be considered in design is the difficulty of assembly from directions other than directly above. The aim of the designer should be to allow for assembly in sandwich or layer fashion, each part being placed on top of the previous one. The biggest advantage of this method is that gravity can be used to assist in the feeding and placing of the parts. It is also desirable to have workheads and feeding devices above the assembly station where they will be accessible in the event of a fault due to the feeding of a defective part. Assembly from above may also assist in the problem of keeping parts in their correct positions during the machine index period when acceleration forces in the horizontal plane might tend to displace them. In this case, with proper product design where the parts are self-locating, the force due to gravity should be sufficient to hold the part until it is fastened or secured.

If assembly from above is not possible then it is probably wise to divide the assembly into sub-assemblies. For example, an exploded view of a power plug is shown in Fig. 9.6 and in the mechanized assembly of this product it would be relatively difficult to position and drive the two cord grip screws from below. The remainder of

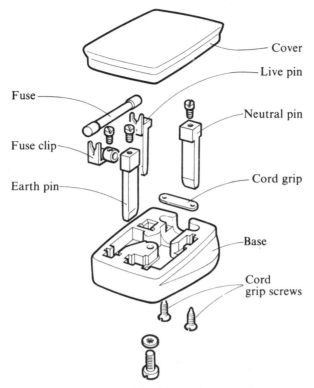

Figure 9.6. Assembly of three-pin power plug.

the assembly (apart from the main holding screw) can be conveniently built into the base from above. In this example the two screws, the cord grip and the plug base could be treated as a sub-assembly dealt with prior to the main assembly machine.

It is always necessary in mechanized assembly to have a base part on which the assembly can be built. This base part must have features which make it suitable for quick and accurate location on the work carrier. Figure 9.7a shows a base part for which it would be difficult to design a suitable work carrier. In this case if a force were applied at A the part would rotate unless adequate clamping were provided. One method of ensuring that a base part is stable is to arrange that its centre of gravity is contained within flat horizontal surfaces. For example, a small ledge machined into the part will allow a simple and efficient work carrier to be designed (Fig. 9.7b).

Location of the base part in the horizontal plane is often achieved by dowel pins mounted in the work carrier. To simplify the assembly of the base part onto the work carrier the dowel pins can be tapered to provide guidance as in the example shown in Fig. 9.8.

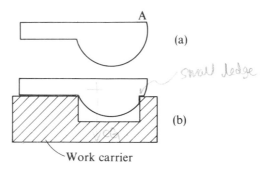

(a)

(b)

Work carrier

Figure 9.7. Design of base part for mounting on work carrier.

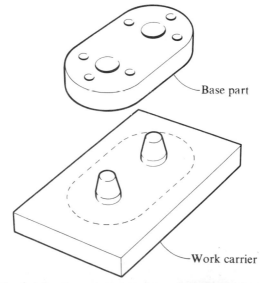

Base part

Work carrier

Figure 9.8. The use of tapered pegs to facilitate assembly.

9.2 Design of Parts for Feeding and Orienting

Many types of parts feeder are used in mechanized assembly, and some of them have been studied in an earlier chapter. Most feeders are suitable for feeding only a very limited range of part shapes and are not generally relevant when discussing the design of parts for feeding and orienting. The most versatile parts feeder is the vibratory bowl feeder and the following section will deal mainly with the aspects of the design of parts which will facilitate feeding and orienting in these devices. Many of the points made, however, will apply equally to other feeding devices.

Parts are generally placed in a hopper feeder in a random fashion and, depending on their shape, will tend to rest on the feeder surfaces in certain ways or attitudes. The process of orientation in the feeder usually consists of rejecting all the parts resting in any way but the one desired or, only selecting and feeding those which are oriented in the desired way. Clearly, a reduction in the number of possible orientations of a part will assist in the feeding and orienting problems and may increase the 'yield' of correctly oriented parts thus improving the efficiency of the feeding device. In chapter 5, which dealt with the orientation of parts, an example was given (Fig. 5.4) of a device to orient machined washers. The probability of these washers being fed chamfered side up is approximately 0·5 and thus the removal of the chamfer, apart from eliminating the need for the orienting device, would double the orienting efficiency. This improvement could either be used to increase the feed rate or reduce the recirculation of washers in the feeder.

Alternatively if a chamfer is necessary it is clear that making this feature as large as possible will facilitate orientation of the part. Tipping[3] suggests that two shapes of part are most easily oriented:

(a) The ideal symmetrical shape which, by its nature, is nearly always fed in its oriented condition. Examples of these are a sphere, a cube, a long cylinder, etc;

(b) A part with marked polar properties of either shape or weight. In these cases either the location of the centre of gravity at one end of the part gives a natural tendency for it to be fed in one particular orientation or the marked asymmetry readily allows for some mechanical means of orientation.

These two ideals may be regarded as the extremes of possible part shape and in between are the whole range of shapes providing orienting problems of varying complexity. The object of the designer should be to arrange that the shape of the part approaches either of these ideals. The example of the elimination of the chamfer on a machined washer is one where the approach is towards symmetry. A further practical example of this would be a stud where the screwed lengths at each end are different (Fig. 9.9a). Re-design of the product could probably be made to allow for a stud having equal screwed lengths at each end (Fig. 9.9b) and would thus solve a very difficult orienting problem.

Other examples of re-design to give symmetry are presented in Figs. 9.10 and 9.11.

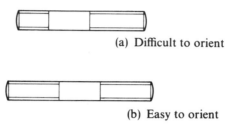

(a) Difficult to orient

(b) Easy to orient

Figure 9.9. Re-design to facilitate orientation.

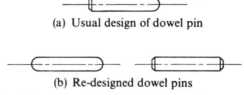

(a) Usual design of dowel pin

(b) Re-designed dowel pins

Figure 9.10. Re-design of dowel pin to facilitate orientation. (After Tipping[3].)

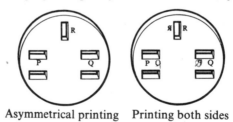

Asymmetrical printing Printing both sides
one side only

Figure 9.11. Further example of re-design to give greater symmetry. (After Iredale[1].)

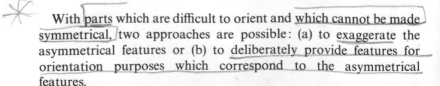

With parts which are difficult to orient and which cannot be made symmetrical, two approaches are possible: (a) to exaggerate the asymmetrical features or (b) to deliberately provide features for orientation purposes which correspond to the asymmetrical features.

One example in the first category is given in Fig. 9.12. This shows a device fitted to a bowl feeder to orient truncated cone shapes. The feature of the part used in this method is the difference in diameter between the top and base of the cone. The vee-shaped cutouts in the feeder track are designed so that a part being fed on its base will pass over the cut-outs whereas one being fed on its top will fall back into the bowl.

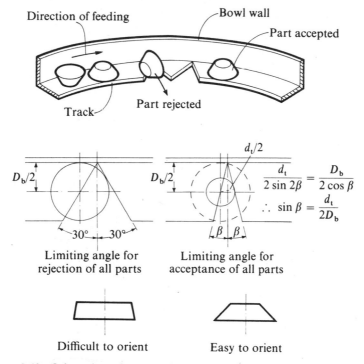

Figure 9.12. Orientation of truncated cone shapes with vee cut-outs in bowl feeder track.

Consideration of the geometry of this device shows that if the half angle of the cut-out is greater than 30 degrees all the parts will be rejected. Further, if the half angle, β, is less than that given by the following equation, all parts are likely to pass over the device. Thus to accept all parts:

$$\sin \beta < d_t/2D_b \qquad (9.1)$$

where D_b is the cone base diameter and d_t is the cone top diameter.

The optimum angle for the cut-outs must lie between these two extremes and clearly if the difference between the cone base and cone top diameters could be made as large as possible, reliable orienting will be more readily achieved. This example is one where the asymmetrical feature of a part might be exaggerated to facilitate orientation. The other approach where asymmetrical features are deliberately added for the purposes of orienting are probably more common and some, given by Iredale[1], are reproduced in Fig. 9.13. In each case the features which require alignment are difficult to utilize in an orienting device so corresponding external features are added deliberately.

Difficult to orient with respect to small holes

Flats on the sides make it much easier to orient with respect to the small holes

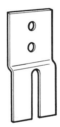

No feature sufficiently significant for orientation

When correctly oriented will hang from rail

Triangular shape of part makes automatic hole orientation difficult

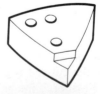

Non-functional shoulder permits proper orientation to be established in a vibratory feeder and maintained in transport rails

Figure 9.13. Provision of asymmetrical features to assist in orientation. (After Iredale[1].)

One very important aspect of design for mechanized assembly is that there should be no tendency for parts to tangle or nest when stored in bulk. If such a tendency exists it can be almost impossible to separate, orient, and feed the parts automatically. Often a small non-functional change in design will prevent this occurrence and some simple examples of this are illustrated in Fig. 9.14.

Clearly with some parts it will not be possible to make design changes which will enable them to be handled automatically. For example, very small parts or complicated shapes formed, perhaps,

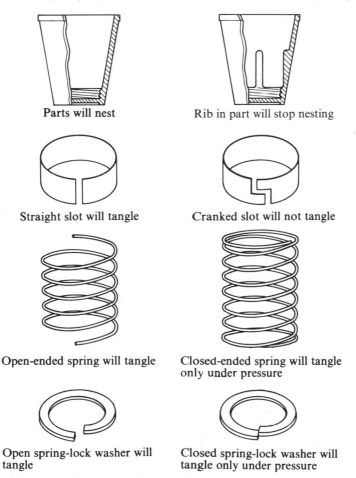

Parts will nest   Rib in part will stop nesting

Straight slot will tangle   Cranked slot will not tangle

Open-ended spring will tangle   Closed-ended spring will tangle
                                   only under pressure

Open spring-lock washer will   Closed spring-lock washer will
tangle   tangle only under pressure

*Figure 9.14. Examples of re-design to prevent nesting or tangling of parts.
(After Iredale*[1]*.)*

from thin strip. In these cases it is sometimes possible to manufacture the parts on the assembly machine or to separate them from the strip at the moment of assembly. Operations like spring winding or blanking out thin sections have been successfully introduced on assembly machines in the past.

9.3 Summary

The various points made in this discussion of parts and product design for mechanized assembly are summarized below in the form of simple rules for the designer.

9.3.1 *Rules for Product Design*

(a) Ensure that the product has a suitable base part on which to build the assembly.

(b) Ensure that the base part has features which will enable it to be readily located in a stable position in the horizontal plane.

(c) If possible, design the product so that it can be built up in layer fashion, each part being assembled from above and positively located so that there is no tendency for it to move under the action of horizontal acceleration forces during the machine index period.

(d) Try to facilitate assembly by providing chamfers or tapers which will help to guide and position the parts in the correct position.

9.3.2 *Rules for the Design of Parts*

(a) Avoid projections, holes or slots which will cause tangling with identical parts when placed in bulk in the feeder. This may be achieved by arranging that the holes or slots are smaller than the projections.

(b) Attempt to make the parts symmetrical to avoid the need for extra orienting devices and the corresponding loss in feeder efficiency.

(c) If symmetry cannot be achieved then exaggerate asymmetrical features in order to facilitate orienting or, alternatively, provide corresponding asymmetrical features which can be used to orient the parts.

(d) See if 'difficult' parts can be supplied in strip form, like electrical terminals, or in stick form like staples. Alternatively consider whether the parts can be manufactured on the assembly machine.

References

1. IREDALE, R. 'Automatic Assembly—Components and Products.' *Metal-working Production*, 8 April 1964.
2. BALDWIN, S. P. 'How to make sure of Easy Assembly.' *Tool and Manufacturing Engineer*, May, 1966, p. 67.
3. TIPPING, W. V. 'Component and Product Design for Mechanized Assembly.' Conference on Assembly, Fastening, and Jointing Techniques and Equipment, P.E.R.A., 1965.

10.

Design of Assembly Machines

The subject of this chapter is one which brings together the results of the work in all the various aspects of mechanized assembly. Using the knowledge resulting from research, development, and experience, the designer of an assembly machine must produce a proposal which combines many requirements. Some of these requirements, such as reliability and durability, are similar to those for any machine tool. However, certain requirements are applicable only to the assembly machine and are mainly a result of the variations in the quality of the component parts to be assembled. It can reasonably be assumed that an assembly machine can be designed which, if it is only fed with carefully inspected parts, will repeatedly perform the necessary assembly operations satisfactorily. Sometimes, unfortunately, the real problems of mechanized assembly only appear when the machine is installed in the factory and the user fills the feeders with his own standard parts containing the usual proportions of defective parts. The possible effects of feeding a defective part into an assembly machine are:

(a) The mechanical workhead may be seriously damaged resulting in several hours or even days of down-time;
(b) The defective parts may jam in the feeder or workhead and result in machine or workhead down-time whilst the fault is cleared;
(c) The part may pass through the feeder and workhead and spoil the assembly thus effectively causing down-time equal to one machine cycle and producing an assembly which must be repaired.

Often, large samples of the parts to be assembled are available when the assembly machine is designed and clearly the designer should take into account, at the design stage, the quality levels of the parts and the possible difficulties resulting from them. Even the choice of basic transfer system can significantly affect the degree of difficulty caused by defective parts and therefore most of the important decisions will be made by the designer before detailed design is considered. Basically the object of the design should be to obtain a minimum down-time on the machine resulting from a defective part being placed in the corresponding feeding device. This was illustrated in chapter 8 which dealt with the economics of assembly machines. Here it was shown that the minimum cost of assembly, $C_t(min)$, obtained when parts of optimum quality level are used, is given by:

$$C_t(min) = Mt/60 + (2n/10)(MBT/60)^{\frac{1}{2}} + \sum A_b \qquad (10.1)$$

where

M = machine operating costs, shillings/min
t = machine cycle time, sec
n = number of automatic workheads
B = factor indicating increased cost of parts with increasing quality level, shillings per part
T = time taken to clear machine fault, sec
A_b = basic cost of part, shillings

Thus any reductions in T, the time taken to clear a fault caused by a defective part, will reduce the assembly costs by reducing the total machine down-time. The first section of this chapter will discuss the various design factors which can help in ensuring minimum down-time due to defective parts and the second section will deal in detail with the design feasibility study of a typical assembly problem.

10.1 Design Factors to Reduce Machine Down-time due to Defective Parts

The first object in designing feeders and mechanisms for use in mechanized assembly is to ensure that the presence of a defective part will not result in damage to the machine. This possibility does not generally exist where the part is moving under the action of its own weight (i.e., sliding down a chute) or being transported on a vibrating conveyor. However, if the part is being moved or placed in a positive way, it is necessary to arrange that the desired motion is provided by an elastic system. In this case if a defective part becomes jammed, motion can be taken up in the spring members.

For example, if a plunger is to position a part in an assembly it would be inadvisable to drive the plunger directly by a cam. In this case it would be better to provide a spring to give the necessary force to drive the plunger and use the cam to withdraw the plunger. With this arrangement a jammed part could not damage the mechanism.

The next object in design should be to ensure that a jammed part can be removed quickly from the machine. This can be facilitated by several means, some of which are listed below:

(a) All feeders, chutes and mechanisms should be readily accessible. Thus external covers and shields should be avoided wherever possible;

(b) Enclosed chutes, feeders, and mechanisms should not be employed.

Clearly, one of the cheapest forms of chute is a tube down which the parts can slide freely to the workhead. However, a jam occurring in a closed tube is difficult to clear. Although probably more expensive to provide, open rails are preferable in this case so that the fault can be detected and cleared quickly;

(c) An immediate indication of the location of a fault is desirable. This may be achieved by arranging that a warning light is switched on and a buzzer operated when any operation fails. If the warning light is positioned at the particular workhead the machine operators will be able to locate the fault quickly.

It is necessary for the machine designer to decide whether to arrange that the machine is stopped in the event of a fault or whether to arrange that the 'spoiled' assembly continues through the machine. The work in chapters 7 and 8 showed that in typical circumstances it is preferable to keep the machine running. However, it would be clearly undesirable to attempt any further operations on the spoiled assembly. For this purpose the 'memory pin' system can be employed where each work carrier is fitted with a pin which, in the event of a failure, is displaced by a lever fitted to the workhead. Each workhead is also provided with a feeler which senses the position of the pin prior to carrying out the operation. If the pin is displaced then the operation is not carried out.

The difficulty with the memory pin system is that it is not possible for the workhead to detect immediately whether a particular fault will be repetitive. One possibility is to arrange that initially any type of fault will displace the memory pin but when say two or three faults have occurred in succession the machine is automatically stopped. Alternatively, it may be left to a machine operator to observe when a succession of faults occurs and for the operator to stop the machine.

The above discussion has dealt with methods of reducing the down-time on a machine caused by defective parts. Clearly, the ideal situation would be when the defective parts are detected and rejected in the feeding devices. Although it is generally not possible to perform complete inspection during the feeding of parts, it is sometimes possible to eliminate a considerable proportion of the defective ones. Figure 10.1 shows an example given by Ward[1] where

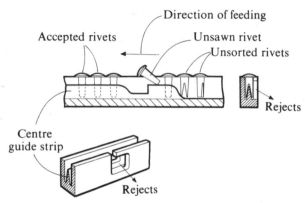

Figure 10.1. System for inspecting bifurcated rivets. (After Ward[1].)

unsawn bifurcated rivets are detected and rejected in a bowl feeder. In this case the device was incorporated to prevent unsawn rivets being fed to the riveting head where they would damage the mechanism during the operation. Sometimes, small pieces of swarf and other foreign bodies find their way into a bowl feeder and a simple way of rejecting these is illustrated in Fig. 10.2. Quite sophisticated inspection arrangements can be built into a bowl feeder and it has been found economical in some circumstances to develop such a device to inspect the parts before they are placed in the assembly machine feeders. In this case the down-time occurs on the inspection device instead of on the assembly machine. This system is unlikely to be economic unless the inspection device is able to supply parts for several workheads or several assembly machines.

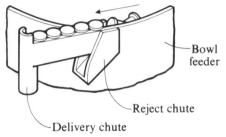

*Figure 10.2. System for rejecting foreign matter in vibratory bowl feeder.
(After Ward[1].)*

10.2   Feasibility Study

The decision to build or purchase a mechanized assembly machine is generally based on the results of a feasibility study. The object of this study is to predict the performance and economics of the proposed machine. In mechanized assembly these predictions are likely to be subject to greater errors than with most other types of production equipment mainly because the machine is probably a 'one-off' and its performance will be very dependent on the qualities of the parts to be assembled. Also, similar machines will not generally be available for study. Nevertheless, a feasibility study must be made and all the knowledge and experience acquired in the past from mechanized assembly projects must be applied to the problem in order to give predictions which are as accurate as possible.

Certain information is clearly required before a study can be made. For example, maximum and minimum production rates during the probable life of the machine must be known. The range of variations in these figures is very important because a single assembly machine is very inflexible. The operators required on the machine must all be present when the machine is working, or, if the machine is stopped due to a fall-off in demand for the product, then they must be employed elsewhere. Thus, mechanized assembly machines are generally only suitable when the volume of production is known to be steady. Further, they can usually only be applied profitably when the volume is high. Tipping[2] suggests that where the volume is 500,000 assemblies per year or more the application of mechanized assembly has an excellent chance of success. Apart from this high volume requirement, the labour costs of the existing assembly process must also be high if mechanized assembly is to be successful.

Clearly much more information will be required and many other factors will combine to determine the final answer and some of these will be dealt with in greater detail below.

10.2.1   Precedence Diagrams

It is always useful, when studying the assembly of a product, to draw a diagram which shows clearly and simply the various ways in which the process may be carried out. In most assemblies there are alternatives in the order in which some of the parts may be assembled. There are also likely to be some parts where no flexibility in order is allowed. For example, in the three-pin power plug shown in Fig. 10.3, the pins may be placed in position in any order but the fuse can only be inserted after the fuse clip and the live pin are in position. Further the cover can only be placed in position and secured after all the remaining parts have been assembled into the base.

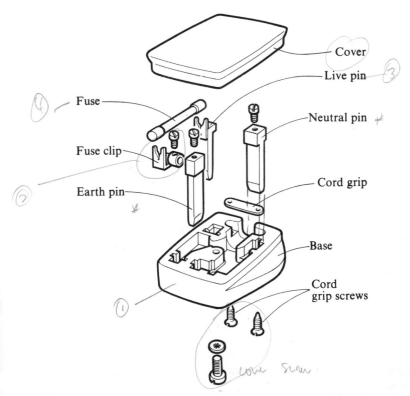

Figure 10.3. Assembly of three-pin power plug.

The precedence diagram is designed to show all these possibilities and its use has been described in detail by Prenting and Battaglin[3]. A precedence diagram for the assembly of the power plug assuming no sub-assemblies are involved is shown in Fig. 10.4 where it can be seen that each individual operation has been assigned a number and is represented by an appropriate circle with the number inscribed. The circles are connected by arrows showing the precedence relations.

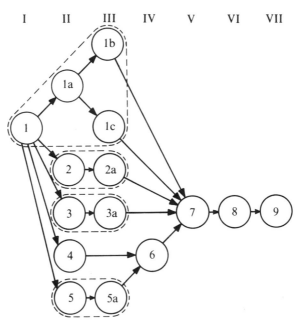

| I | II | III | IV | V | VI | VII |

1. Load base onto work carrier
1a. Cord grip
1b. Cord grip screw
1c. Cord grip screw
2. Earth pin
2a. Earth pin screw
3. Neutral pin
3a. Neutral pin screw

4. Live pin
5. Fuse clip
5a. Fuse clip screw
6. Fuse
7. Cover
8. Cover screw
9. Remove complete assembly

Figure 10.4. Precedence diagram for complete assembly of power plug.

In drawing the precedence diagram, all the operations which can be carried out first are placed in column I. Usually only one operation appears in this column—the placing of the base part on the work carrier. Operations which can only be performed when at least one of the operations in column I has been performed are placed in column II. Lines are then drawn from each operation in column II to the preceding operations in column I. In the example in Fig. 10.4, none of the column II operations can be performed until the base of the power plug has been placed on the work carrier and therefore lines are drawn connecting operations 1a, 2, 3, 4, and 5 to operation 1. Third stage operations are then placed in column III with appropriate connecting lines and so on until the diagram is complete. Thus following all the lines from a given operation to the left indicates all the operations which must be completed before the operation under consideration can be performed.

In the assembly of the power plug there are 15 operations and it will probably be impracticable to carry out all these on a single machine. For example, it would be difficult to assemble the cord grip and the two cord grip screws whilst the plug base is held in a work carrier because these parts enter the base from different directions. It is probably better therefore to treat these parts as a sub-assembly and this is indicated in Fig. 10.4 by the dotted line enclosing the necessary operations. In a similar way the neutral and earth pins and the fuse clip together with their respective screws can also be treated as sub-assemblies. These groups of operations are all indicated by the dotted lines in the figure.

One of the objects in designing a mechanized assembly machine should be to include as few operations as possible on the line in order to keep machine down-time to a minimum. It is desirable therefore to break the product down into the smallest number of sub-assemblies and carry out individual studies of the sub-assemblies. If these can be mechanically assembled then separate machines may be used. These machines can then be arranged to feed the main assembly machine at the appropriate point.

Figure 10.5 shows the precedence diagram for the sub-assemblies of the power plug. It can be seen that no flexibility exists in the ordering of operations 1, 7, 8, and 9. The operations 2, 3, 4, 5, and 6, however, can be carried out in any order between operations 1 and 7 except that 6 cannot be performed until both 4 and 5 are completed. Considering the group of operations 4, 5, and 6 first there are two ways in which these can be performed; either 4, 5, 6 or 5, 4, 6. Operation 3 could be performed at any stage in this order giving $4 \times 2 = 8$ possibilities. Finally operation 2 could be performed at any stage in the ordering of operations 3, 4, 5, and 6 giving a total of $5 \times 8 = 40$ possibilities. Thus the precedence diagram shown in

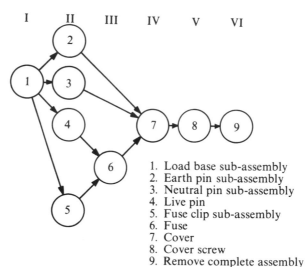

1. Load base sub-assembly
2. Earth pin sub-assembly
3. Neutral pin sub-assembly
4. Live pin
5. Fuse clip sub-assembly
6. Fuse
7. Cover
8. Cover screw
9. Remove complete assembly

Figure 10.5. Precedence diagram for assembly of power plug.

Fig. 10.5 represents 40 possible orderings of the various assembly operations.

In a fixed-cycle or indexing assembly machine, the order of assembly may not be a very important factor but the chosen order of assembly in a free-transfer machine can have an effect on the machine's performance. However, before these questions can be considered it will be necessary to estimate the quality levels of the parts to be assembled.

10.2.2 *Quality Levels of Parts*

If assembly of a completely new product is to be contemplated then the estimation of the quality levels of the parts may be extremely difficult, if not impossible. However, a large proportion of assembly machine feasibility studies are concerned with existing products and in these cases experiments can be performed to determine the quality levels of the various parts. It should always be remembered in such a study that defective parts do not generally create great difficulties when assembly is by hand. The operator can often quickly detect and reject a defective part and in many cases, when the so called defective part is simply a foreign body such as a piece of swarf or a cigarette end, the operator will not even attempt to pick it up but will simply leave it in the parts container to be discarded later. This means that a study of quality level must be conducted at the existing assembly stations where the numbers of discarded parts and foreign bodies can be recorded. A further danger is that many engineers responsible for assembly processes assume that 100 per cent visual inspection results in 100 per cent acceptable parts. The assumption that an operator inspecting every part which is to be subsequently assembled will detect every defective part is clearly not valid.

The best procedure in estimating quality levels is for the investigator to sit with the assembly operators for a substantial period of time and note every defective part or foreign body which is discarded. Obviously it will be inadvisable to assume that the quality levels recorded cannot be improved upon but it will be necessary to estimate the cost of these improvements and allow for this extra cost in the feasibility study.

Having noted the number of defective parts in a given batch it will then be possible for the investigator to divide these into two categories: (a) those parts which cannot be assembled, for example, screws with no thread or slot; (b) those parts which can be assembled but are normally rejected by the operator, for example, discoloured or chipped parts.

The number of parts falling within the first category will allow estimates to be made of the assembly machine down-time and those falling within the second category will allow estimates to be made of the number of unacceptable or defective assemblies produced by the machine.

A hypothetical set of figures for the power plug shown in Fig. 10.3 are presented in Table 10.1. It is very important to remember that no assessment can be made of the most suitable type of assembly machine or of the number of operations which can economically be performed mechanically, until the individual quality levels of the various parts have been investigated.

10.2.3   *Parts Feeding and Assembly*

An estimate must now be made of the degree of difficulty with which the individual parts can be automatically fed and assembled. It should be noted here that for each operation four possibilities exist, namely:

(a) Automatic feeding and assembly;
(b) Manual feeding and automatic assembly;
(c) Automatic feeding and manual assembly;
(d) Manual feeding and assembly.

TABLE 10.1

Quality Levels of Power Plug Parts (Hypothetical)

Parts	Fault	Number of faults in assembling 10,000 plugs	Percentage faults
Base sub-assembly	Chipped	10	0·10
	Earth pin will not assemble	170	1·70
	Live pin will not assemble	20	0·20
	Neutral pin will not assemble	30	0·30
Earth pin sub-assembly	No screw	41	0·41
Neutral pin sub-assembly	No screw	59	0·59
Live pin	Fuse will not assemble	123	1·23
	Fuse assembles unsatisfactorily	21	0·21
Fuse clip sub-assembly	Fuse will not assemble	115	1·15
	Fuse assembles unsatisfactorily	17	0·17
Fuse	Damaged	18	0·18
Cover	Chipped	10	0·10
	Cover screw hole blocked	200	2·00
Cover screw	No thread or slot	20	0·20

At this stage in the feasibility study it may be necessary to resort to experiment. In considering the feeding of parts, all but the simplest shapes will probably require a vibratory bowl feeder and simple experiments can normally be performed to test various ideas for orienting and feeding. Estimates can then be made of the various feed rates possible. For a given bowl feeder the maximum feed rate obtainable is proportional to the reciprocal of the length of the part, assuming that all parts arrive at the bowl outlet, end to end. Thus, with large parts which have many possible orientations, only one of which will be required, the feed rate of oriented parts can be very low.

For example, both the base and top of the power plug shown in Fig. 10.3 are approximately 2 in. long and can be fed up a bowl feeder track in any of eight possible orientations. Thus, if suitable devices were fitted to the track of the bowl to reject seven of the eight orientations and the bowl has a maximum useful conveying velocity of 2 in/sec, then the maximum possible feed rate of oriented parts will be given by:

$$F_{max} = 60v_m/lz \text{ parts/min} \qquad (10.2)$$

where

v_m = mean conveying velocity, in/sec,
l = length of part, in.,

and

z = number of possible stable orientations of the part.

Thus:

$$F_{max} = \frac{2 \times 60}{2 \times 8} = 7\cdot5 \text{ parts/min}$$

In this simple example it has been assumed that the part is square and that an equal possibility exists of the part being conveyed in each of its eight possible modes of orientation. Clearly this will not always be true and if the orienting devices are designed to reject the modes of least probability then the maximum feed rate can be increased. Further, if active orienting devices are fitted which can correct some of the undesired orientations then the 'yield' of correctly oriented parts can be increased. The possibility also exists that some simple change in the design of the parts will either reduce the number of orientations or increase the probability of the desired orientation.

Bearing all these points in mind, the investigator will make his decision as to whether automatic feeding of the particular part is feasible. In the example of the power plug it is possible that the base sub-assemblies and cover could not be fed at the required rate, and that the fuse clip assembly, because of its complicated shape, could not be handled by automatic means. The remaining parts and sub-assemblies could probably all be fed and assembled automatically with bowl feeders and placing mechanisms, with the exception of the main holding screw. This could be fed and screwed from below with a proprietary automatic screwdriver.

10.2.4 *Machine Layout and Performance*

Three main possibilities exist for the layout of the assembly machine, namely: (a) in-line indexing; (b) rotary indexing; (c) in-line free-transfer.

(a) *In-line indexing machine.* If it is assumed that the base, top, and fuse clip are to be assembled manually on a straight in-line machine, then at least two operators will be required on the assembly machine. The first, positioned at the beginning of the line, could place the base sub-assembly on the work carrier and place the fuse clip assembly in the base (operations 1 and 5 of Fig. 10.5 respectively). The second operator could assemble the cover and remove the complete plug assembly from the end of the line (operations 7 and 9 of Fig. 10.5 respectively).

It is generally necessary on an assembly machine to include some inspection stations. In the present example, it is clear that, after the plug cover has been assembled, there will be no simple means of inspecting for the presence of the fuse clip, fuse, and the three small screws in the neutral and earth pins and the fuse clip. Thus it will be necessary to include an inspection head on the machine immediately before operation 7 (the assembly of the cover), which will check for the presence of all these parts.

In the present example it will also be necessary to decide whether the inspection head should be designed to stop the machine in the event of a fault or to prevent further operations being performed on the assembly. In the hypothetical studies presented for each design of machine it will be assumed that the memory pin system is incorporated where the inspection head will be designed to operate the memory pin rather than stop the machine.

The general layout of a typical in-line indexing machine is shown in Fig. 10.6. It will be noted that operations 4 and 6 have been arranged directly after the first (operator) station. This is to minimize the possibility of the fuse clip becoming displaced during the machine index. When the fuse is in position, the fuse clip is then positively retained. These desirable features provide further restrictions in the order of assembly and the precedence diagram is modified to that shown in Fig. 10.7.

The down-time on an indexing machine is given by the sum of the down-times on the individual heads due to the feeding of defective parts plus the effective down-time due to the production of unacceptable assemblies.

If, for each machine station, x per cent is the effective proportion of defective to acceptable parts, then mx per cent is the average number of defectives which will cause a machine stoppage and $(1 - m)x$ per cent is the effective average number of defectives which will spoil the assembly but not stop the machine. The down-time

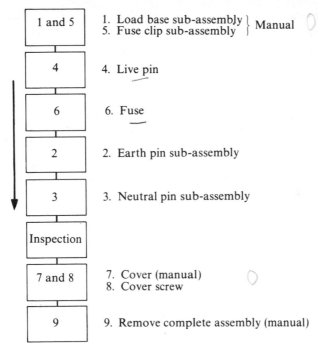

Figure 10.6. Station layout of in-line indexing machine for assembling power plugs.

due to machine stoppages and the final production rate are found as follows:

In producing N assemblies the number of machine stoppages is $N\Sigma mx/100$ where Σmx is the sum of the individual values of mx for the automatic workheads.

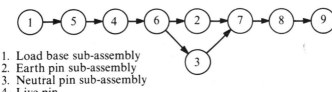

1. Load base sub-assembly
2. Earth pin sub-assembly
3. Neutral pin sub-assembly
4. Live pin
5. Fuse clip sub-assembly
6. Fuse
7. Cover
8. Cover screw
9. Remove complete assembly

Figure 10.7. Final precedence diagram for assembly of power plug.

If T is the average time to correct a fault and restart the machine then the down-time due to machine stoppages is $NT\Sigma mx/100$ and if t is the machine cycle time then the percentage down-time, D, will be given by:

$$D = \sum mx/(t/T + \sum mx/100) \text{ per cent} \qquad (10.3)$$

The figures in Table 10.1 are re-arranged in Table 10.2 to give the effective quality levels for the various operations. From these figures it can be seen that the value of $\sum mx$ is 6·78 per cent and assuming that $t = 3$ sec (the time taken to place the base and assemble the fuse clip manually) and $T = 15$ sec (a typical figure in practice), then:

$$D = \frac{6·78}{0·2 + 0·0678} = 25·2 \text{ per cent}$$

During the time the machine is operating some of the assemblies produced will contain defective parts which did not stop the machine

TABLE 10.2

Effective Quality Levels in Assembly of Power Plug

Operation	Automatic station on free-transfer machine	Effective quality level x per cent	Ratio of defectives causing machine stoppages (m)	mx	$(1-m)x$
1 Assemble base sub-assembly onto work carrier	—	0·10	0	0	0·1
2 Assemble earth pin S.A. into base	4	1·70	1·0	1·7	0
3 Assemble neutral pin S.A. into base	3	0·30	1·0	0·3	0
4 Assemble live pin into base	1	0·20	1·0	0·2	0
5 Assemble fuse clip S.A. into base	—	0	0	0	0
6 Assemble fuse into live pin and fuse clip	2	2·94	0·813	2·38	0·56
7 Assemble cover	5	0·10	0	0	0·1
8 Assemble cover screw	5	2·20	1·0	2·2	0
9 Remove complete assembly	—	0	—	—	—
Inspection	—	1·00	0	0	1·0

and assuming that no assembly contains more than one such defective part then the production rate of acceptable assemblies, P_a, will be given by:

$$P_a = (60/t)(1 - \sum (1 - m)x/100)(1 - D/100) \qquad (10.4)$$

From Table 10.2, $\sum(1 - m)x = 1.76$ per cent and therefore from eq. (10.4):

$$P_a = \frac{60}{3}(0.9824)0.748 = 14.7 \text{ assemblies/min}$$

(b) *Rotary indexing machine.* The basic layout of a suitable rotary indexing machine is shown in Fig. 10.8. It has been assumed in this case that operations 1, 5, 7, and 9 would all be carried out by a single operator with an increased machine time cycle of $t = 3.2$ sec.

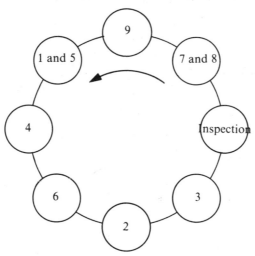

1. Load base sub-assembly (manual)
2. Earth pin sub-assembly
3. Neutral pin sub-assembly
4. Live pin
5. Fuse clip sub-assembly (manual)
6. Fuse
7. Cover (manual)
8. Cover screw
9. Remove complete assembly (manual)

Figure 10.8. Station layout of rotary indexing machine for assembling power plugs.

It is commonly accepted that six is the practical maximum number of stations on a rotary indexing machine and it can be seen that in the present example eight stations are required. For this reason it may be decided that the machine will be too 'crowded' with equipment to allow sufficient accessibility to the various points where parts may become jammed. The effect of this will be to increase the value of T and it will be assumed in the following analysis that T is increased to 16 sec, thus maintaining the ratio $t/T = 0.2$ as with the in-line indexing machine.

The machine down-time due to stoppages will remain at 25·2 per cent as in the previous example but since $t = 3.2$ sec, the production rate of acceptable assemblies given by eq. (10.4) will change to

$$P_a = \frac{60}{3.2}(0.9824)0.748 = 13.8 \text{ assemblies/min}$$

(c) *In-line free-transfer machine.* The design of a free-transfer machine suitable for assembling the power plug is shown in Fig. 10.9.

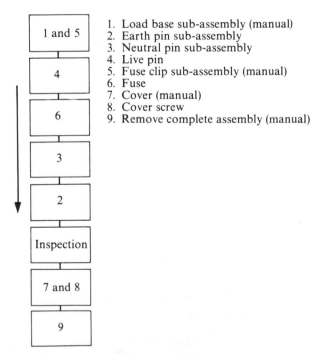

1. Load base sub-assembly (manual)
2. Earth pin sub-assembly
3. Neutral pin sub-assembly
4. Live pin
5. Fuse clip sub-assembly (manual)
6. Fuse
7. Cover (manual)
8. Cover screw
9. Remove complete assembly (manual)

Figure 10.9. Station layout of free-transfer assembly machine for assembling power plugs.

Progress has recently been made in reducing the high cost of free-transfer machines by a unit construction principle. In this case, it is necessary to standardize on the size of buffer stock and it will be assumed in the following that each unit of the machine is capable of accommodating five work carriers, one of which is situated below the workhead, the remaining four comprising the buffer stock for the workhead.

Analysis of this type of machine has already been made in chapters 7 and 8 and the equations presented in Table 10.3 apply to the present example.

In the equations the effect of the first and last operations has been ignored since these operations of placing the base and fuse clip into the work carrier and removing the completed assembly will not generally cause down-time on the machine. Operation 2 has been positioned nearer the end of the machine than operation 3 since operation 3 deals with parts of a higher quality level. This follows from the work in chapter 8 which indicated that in order to obtain minimum down-time, operations involving parts with poor effective quality levels should be positioned as near to either end of the machine as possible.

Two operators will be required on the machine under consideration and the original times of $t = 3$ sec, $T = 15$ sec will be applicable.

Substitution in the equations in Table 10.3 of the appropriate values of m_1x_1 to m_5x_5 inclusive from Table 10.2 and writing $b = 4$ leads to the following values of a_1 to a_4:

$$a_1 = 3 \cdot 88 \quad a_2 = 2 \cdot 48 \quad a_3 = 2 \cdot 3 \quad a_4 = 1 \cdot 3$$

It is now found that, with these values, the last term in the first two equations, the first term in the third and fourth equations and the first two terms in the last equation must now be omitted because they become negative. Re-solving the equations now gives:

$$a_1 = 3 \cdot 82, \quad a_2 = 2 \cdot 51, \quad a_3 = 2 \cdot 37, \quad a_4 = 2 \cdot 04$$

Substitution of these results in the last equation with the first two terms omitted gives:

$$\frac{100d}{Nt} = 0 \cdot 59 \times 0 \cdot 3 + 2 \cdot 96 \times 1 \cdot 7 + 5 \times 2 \cdot 2 = 16 \cdot 23$$

Thus

$$D = \frac{16 \cdot 23}{1 + 0 \cdot 1623} = 13 \cdot 9 \text{ per cent}$$

TABLE 10.3

General Equations for the Down-time, d, at each Station of the Five Station Assembly Machine when Producing N Assemblies

Work-head	Down-time due to First workhead	Second workhead	Third workhead	Fourth workhead	Fifth workhead
First, $\dfrac{100d_1}{N} = Tm_1x_1$	$+[T-(b-a_1)t]m_2x_2$	$+[T-(2b-a_1-a_2)t]m_3x_3$	$+[T-(3b-a_1-a_2-a_3)t]m_4x_4$	$+[T-(4b-a_1-a_2-a_3-a_4)t]m_5x_5$	
Second, $\dfrac{100d_2}{N} = [T-a_1t]m_1x_1$	$+Tm_2x_2$	$+[T-(b-a_2)t]m_3x_3$	$+[T-(2b-a_2-a_3)t]m_4x_4$	$+[T-(3b-a_2-a_3-a_4)t]m_5x_5$	
Third, $\dfrac{100d_3}{N} = [T-(a_1+a_2)t]m_1x_1$	$+[T-a_2t]m_2x_2$	$+Tm_3x_3$	$+[T-(b-a_3)t]m_4x_4$	$+[T-(2b-a_3-a_4)t]m_5x_5$	
Fourth, $\dfrac{100d_4}{N} = [T-(a_1+a_2+a_3)t]m_1x_1$	$+[T-(a_2+a_3)t]m_2x_2$	$+[T-a_3t]m_3x_3$	$+Tm_4x_4$	$+[T-(b-a_4)t]m_5x_5$	
Fifth, $\dfrac{100d_5}{N} = [T-(a_1+a_2+a_3+a_4)t]m_1x_1$	$+[T-(a_2+a_3+a_4)t]m_2x_2$	$+[T-(a_3+a_4)t]m_3x_3$	$+[T-a_4t]m_4x_4$	$+Tm_5x_5$	

where D is the percentage down-time due to machine stoppages. The production rate of acceptable assemblies will again be given by eq. (10.4) thus:

$$P_a = \frac{60}{3}(0.9824)(1 - 0.139) = 16.9 \text{ assemblies/min}$$

10.2.5 Economics of the Various Machines

Having estimated the effective production rate for each type of machine, it is now possible to make comparisons of their economics.

The approach made here will be to assume that in the particular company concerned, an estimate can be made of the amount of capital which can be economically spent to replace each operator. Some companies put this figure at £1,000 but clearly the economic amount can vary considerably depending on the operator overheads, availability of labour, and the amortization period for the proposed machine.

For each machine considered above, the number of acceptable assemblies produced in one day will be estimated. The extra number of operators required to produce this number of assemblies in the same period will then be calculated. It will be assumed that, on average, one operator can assemble 1,000 plugs in one eight-hour shift using the same sub-assemblies and parts as the proposed machine, and provided with a jig and all other necessary aids costing £300 per operator. These figures, although hypothetical, are considered realistic and clearly in a practical feasibility study, it is important to obtain an accurate estimate of the operator costs and production rate with the manual process.

For each type of machine the various feeders, workheads, and inspection devices are identical; the only variation being in the transfer device employed. In all, five automatic workheads and one inspection head are required and these will be assumed to cost a total of £2,000 irrespective of the type of transfer machine.

Table 10.4 gives the assumed costs of the three transfer machines studied above, including control unit, work carriers, and, where appropriate, work carrier return system together with the effective production rate and the number of operators required. In each case one operator has been allowed for correcting machine faults and filling the feeders at regular intervals.

The economics for each machine are also presented in Table 10.4.

With the purely hypothetical figures used in the example, the rotary index machine would appear to be the most economic.

TABLE 10.4

Economics of Various Transfer Machines in Power Plug Assembly

		In-line index	Rotary index	Free transfer
1	Cost of transfer device and work carriers	£6000	£5000	£7000
2	Cost of workheads, etc.	£2000	£2000	£2000
3	Total cost of machine (1) + (2)	£8000	£7000	£9000
4	Effective production rate, assemblies per minute	14·7	13·8	16·9
5	Number of operators	3	2	3
6	Number of assemblies produced in an eight-hour shift	7050	6610	8120
7	Number of operators required to produce (6) manually	7·0	6·6	8·1
8	Cost of equipment for manual operation ((7) × £300)	£2100	£1980	£2430
9	Effective cost of machine	£5900	£5020	£6570
10	Number of operators saved	4·0	4·6	5·1
11	Capital outlay per operator (9) ÷ (10)	£1470	£1090	£1290

However, there was some doubt whether the eight stations required could be arranged round one rotary indexing machine and if this were not possible then the free-transfer machine would be preferred.

Clearly in a practical situation other factors such as incentive schemes, availability of operators, etc., would need to be taken into account but it is hoped that the above example will serve as a rough guide to the procedure for carrying out a feasibility study for mechanized assembly.

References

1. WARD, K. A. 'Fastening methods in Mechanized Assembly.' Paper presented at the Conference on Mechanized Assembly, July, 1966, Royal College of Advanced Technology, Salford.
2. TIPPING, W. V. 'Design of Mechanized Assembly Lines.' Paper presented at the Conference on Mechanized Assembly, July, 1966, Royal College of Advanced Technology, Salford.
3. PRENTING, T. O. and BATTAGLIN, R. M. 'The Precedence Diagram: A Tool for Analysis in Assembly Line Balancing.' *The Journal of Industrial Engineering*, vol. 15, no. 4. July–August, 1964, p. 208.

Appendix I

Out-of-phase Vibratory Conveyors

Experimental and theoretical investigations[1] have shown that certain fundamental limitations exist in the performance of conventional vibratory feeders namely:

(a) The conveying velocity of parts up the inclined track is always less than that of parts travelling round the flat bowl base. This means that motion of parts on the track is normally obtained through the pushing action of those circulating round the bowl bottom. With this situation there is a tendency for parts to jam in the various selecting and orienting devices fitted to the bowl track.

Some parts, because of their shape, are difficult to feed under these circumstances. For example very thin sheet parts are not able to push each other up the track. In this case the feed rate obtained with a conventional bowl feeder is very low.

Sometimes it is necessary, as part of the orienting system, to have a discontinuity in the track. Again because the parts travelling round the bottom of the bowl cannot push those on the track beyond the discontinuity, the feed rate is generally unsatisfactory;

(b) The conveying velocity of parts in a conventional vibratory bowl feeder is very sensitive to changes in the coefficient of friction between the part and the track and conveying velocities are very low with low coefficients of friction;

(c) For high feed rates, it is necessary for the parallel velocity of the track to be high. However, because of the method of driving a conventional vibratory bowl feeder, an increase in the amplitude of the parallel component of vibration must be accompanied by a corresponding increase in the amplitude of the normal component of vibration. This latter increase is undesirable because as the normal track acceleration increases above the value which causes the component to 'hop' along the track, the mode of conveying quickly becomes erratic and unstable due to the bouncing of parts on impact with the track.

A new drive is now described which is suitable for all types of vibratory conveyors and which solves many of the problems associated with conventional designs.

I.1　Out-of-phase Conveying

The new method for driving vibratory feeding devices is based on the idea that the normal and parallel components of motion of the track should have independent amplitude control and should be out-of-phase. Under these circumstances the locus of a point on the track becomes elliptical instead of linear.

Theoretical and experimental work has been conducted on this new type of drive[1] and some of its advantages can be demonstrated by means of the results shown in Fig. I.1. In the figure, the product

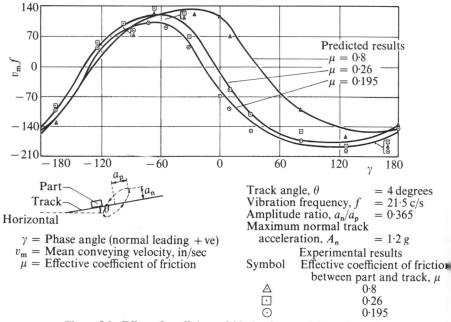

Figure I.1. Effect of coefficient of friction in out-of-phase conveying.

of the mean conveying velocity, v_m, and the frequency of vibration, f, is plotted against the phase difference, γ between the two components of motion. In the results illustrated, the ratio of the normal, a_n, and the parallel, a_p, amplitudes of vibration and the normal track acceleration were both kept constant. The relationships are plotted for three values of the coefficient of friction, μ, between the part and the track which cover the range likely to be met in practice.

It can be seen from the figure that when the phase angle was zero, simulating a conventional feeder, the conveying velocity was very sensitive to changes in μ. Further, for values of μ less than 0·3, the part was moving backward. The results show that if the track parallel motion leads the track normal motion by 65 degrees, the conveying velocity becomes uniformly high for all the values of μ considered.

Figure I.2 shows the predicted effect on the mean conveying velocity, v_m of changing γ in the relevant range (-90 degrees to 0 degrees) for three values of the amplitude ratio a_n/a_p, and when the normal track acceleration A_n was kept constant. In these results a track angle of 4 degrees and a coefficient of friction of 0·2 were chosen because it was considered that these represented the most severe conditions likely to be encountered in practice. It is clear from the figure that, for conventional conveying, as a_p is increased, indicating an increase in the maximum parallel track velocity, the backward conveying velocity of the parts increases. However, for the optimum phase angle ($\gamma = -65$ degrees) the forward conveying

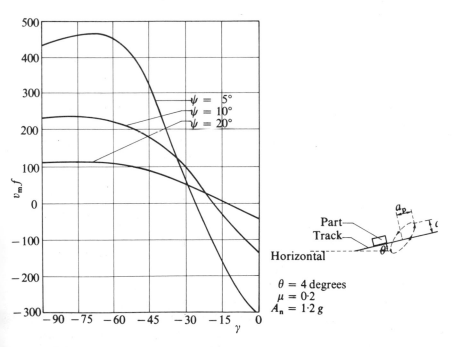

Figure I.2. Predicted effect of amplitude ratio ($a_n/a_p = \tan \psi$) in out-of-phase conveying.

velocity is increased as a result of an increase in a_p. It is also of interest to note that if the vibration frequency was 25 c/s, (for which a control system has been designed) a conveying velocity as high as 18 in/sec can be achieved.

The above results show that definite advantages are to be gained from operating a vibratory bowl feeder under the optimum 'out-of-phase' conditions. First, the high conveying velocities attainable are almost independent of the nature of the parts being conveyed. Second, because the feed rate can be controlled by adjusting the parallel component of vibration only, the track normal acceleration may be held constant at a level which does not cause erratic movement of the parts (in the results presented the normal track acceleration was $1.2 \, g$ which represents stable conveying for most materials). Third, if a_p were to be gradually increased as the part climbs the track, the conveying velocity of the part would gradually increase. This would result in separation of the parts as they climb the track. This situation can be achieved in practice by gradually increasing the track radius and would result in more efficient orienting and greater reliability in operation.

I.2   Practical Applications

Figure I.3 shows an exploded view of a vibratory bowl feeder designed to operate on the principle outlined above. In this design, motion normal to the track is imparted to the bowl through an intermediate plate supported on the base. Motion parallel to the track is obtained through the springs which support the bowl on the plate. With a suitable controller, the two independent motions will have the required phase difference and the situation described for out-of-phase conveying can be obtained.

Tests conducted on a bowl feeder based on the design proposed above have verified the findings of the research. As a practical example of the capabilities of the new design of feeder, an attempt was made to feed thin mica specimens which a manufacturer had previously found almost impossible to feed in a typical conventional vibratory bowl feeder. With the new feeder, however, it was possible to feed these specimens separately up the track at conveying velocities of up to 18 in/sec without any erratic motion.

The new type of drive, suitable for all types of vibratory conveyors and called an out-of-phase drive, has many practical advantages. With this type of drive greater flexibility in performance can be

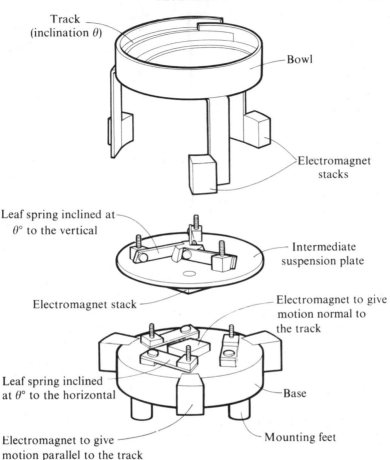

Figure I.3. Exploded view of a vibratory bowl feeder which has independent motion normal and parallel to the bowl track.

achieved, more reliable yet more sophisticated orienting devices can be employed and much higher feed rates can be obtained than with the conventional system. (Note: the out-of-phase drive for vibratory conveyors has been patented by the National Research Development Corporation to whom inquiries for permission to manufacture should be made.)

Reference

1. Redford, A. H. 'Vibratory Conveyors.' Ph.D. Thesis, Royal College of Advanced Technology, Salford, 1966.

Appendix II

Laboratory Experiments

This Appendix gives a complete description of two typical laboratory experiments which may be included in a college or university course on mechanized assembly. The first experiment is designed to illustrate certain practical aspects of the performance of a vibratory bowl feeder; it also indicates how the results of the tests are best presented in order to gain the maximum information. Clearly, similar experiments could be designed to study the performance of other types of parts feeding device employed in mechanized assembly. The second experiment illustrates how the coefficient of dynamic friction between small parts and a feed track may be obtained. This information is used in the second part of the experiment to verify the predictions of the theoretical analysis of a horizontal delivery gravity feed track presented in chapter 6.

II.1 Performance of a Vibratory Bowl Feeder

II.1.1 *Object*

To determine (a) the relationship between vibration amplitude and feed rate for a constant bowl load and (b) the effect of bowl loading on the performance of a vibratory bowl feeder.

II.1.2 *Equipment*

Vibratory bowl feeder, (10 in. or 12 in. bowl); 1,000 mild-steel parts $\frac{5}{16}$ in. dia. × 1 in. long; Transducer arranged to measure the vertical component of the bowl vibration amplitude; Stop watch.

II.1.3 *Procedure*

(a) For a range of settings on the bowl amplitude control and with a bowl load of 500 parts, measurements are made of the time taken for a part to travel between two marks scribed on the inside of the bowl. The vertical vibration amplitude of the bowl is also measured and in these tests a device is fitted to the top of the bowl track which continuously returns the parts to the bottom of the bowl in order to maintain the bowl load constant.

(b) Commencing with the bowl full (1,000 parts) and the amplitude control set to give a low feed rate (less than one part per second) the times are measured for successive batches of 100 parts to be delivered. In this test the parts are allowed to pass down the delivery chute and the readings are continued until the bowl becomes empty.

II.1.4   Theory

Theoretical and experimental work has shown that the parameters which affect the mean conveying velocity, v_m, in vibratory conveying are:

(a) Maximum track acceleration, A, in/sec^2;
(b) Operating frequency, ω, rad/sec;
(c) Track angle, θ (see Fig. II.1);
(d) Vibration angle, ψ (see Fig. II.1);
(e) Coefficient of friction between component and track, μ;
(f) Acceleration due to gravity, g, in/sec^2.

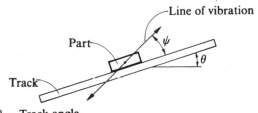

θ = Track angle
ψ = Vibration angle

Figure II.1. Section of track in vibratory bowl feeder.

Dimensional analysis may now be applied to this problem as follows: Let

$$v_m^{a_1} = f[A^{a_2}, \omega^{a_3}, \theta^{a_4}, \psi^{a_5}, \mu^{a_6}, g^{a_7}] \qquad (II.1)$$

Using the fundamental dimensions of length (L) and time (T) we may now write

$$\left(\frac{L}{T}\right)^{a_1} = f\left[\left(\frac{L}{T^2}\right)^{a_2}, \left(\frac{1}{T}\right)^{a_3}, \left(\frac{L}{T^2}\right)^{a_7}\right] \qquad (II.2)$$

Thus for eq. (II.1) to be dimensionally homogeneous we have

$$\left.\begin{array}{rl} a_1 = & a_2 + a_7 \\ -a_1 = & -2a_2 - a_3 - 2a_7 \end{array}\right\} \tag{II.3}$$

or

and

$$\left.\begin{array}{rl} a_7 = & a_1 - a_2 \\ a_3 = & -a_1 \end{array}\right\} \tag{II.4}$$

Substituting eqs. (II.4) in eq. (II.1) we have

$$v_m^{a_1} = f[A^{a_2}, \omega^{-a_1}, \theta^{a_4}, \psi^{a_5}, \mu^{a_6}, g^{(a_1 - a_2)}]$$

or

$$\frac{v_m \omega}{g} = \phi\left[\left(\frac{A}{g}\right), \theta, \psi, \mu\right] \tag{II.5}$$

Thus for a given bowl and given parts, the dimensionless conveying velocity, $v_m \omega / g$, is a function of the dimensionless maximum track acceleration, A/g. The theoretical work described in chapter 3 shows that it is more convenient to employ the component, A_n, of acceleration normal to the track. However, it was also shown that conveying is generally achieved by the pushing action of the parts circulating around the flat bowl base. In this case, the effective track angle is zero and therefore A, in the analysis above, should be taken as the vertical component, A_v, of the bowl acceleration.

If it is assumed that the bowl moves with simple harmonic motion then the maximum bowl acceleration may be obtained from measurements of the vertical bowl amplitude and a knowledge of the operating frequency, ω.

In the second part of the experiment the mean feed rate, F_0, for a small increment in bowl load will be given by:

$$F_0 = 100/t_f \text{ parts/sec} \tag{II.6}$$

where t_f is the time taken to feed 100 parts.

II.1.5 *Presentation of results*

Figures II.2 and II.3 show results obtained with a typical commercial bowl feeder. In Fig. II.2, the dimensionless mean conveying velocity $v_m \omega / g$ is plotted against the dimensionless vertical bowl acceleration, A_v/g. It can be seen that feeding occurs for all values of A_v/g greater than 0·32 and from this it is possible to estimate the

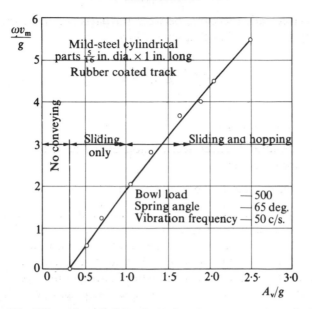

Figure II.2. Effect of vertical bowl acceleration on conveying velocity for a commercial vibratory bowl feeder.

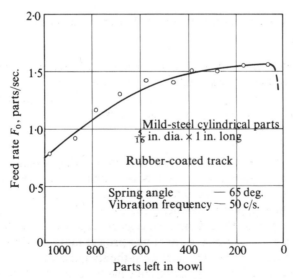

Figure II.3. Load sensitivity of commercial vibratory bowl feeder.

coefficient of static friction μ_s between the parts and the track using the analysis described in chapter 3. Thus:

$$\mu_s = \frac{\cot \psi}{g/A_0 - 1} \qquad \text{(II.7)}$$

where

ψ = vibration angle

A_0 = minimum vertical acceleration of the bowl for feeding to occur, in/sec^2

g = acceleration due to gravity, in/sec^2

In the results presented here, μ_s was estimated to be $0{\cdot}95$ for a mild-steel part in a rubber-coated bowl.

Figure II.3 shows the changes in feed rate, F as the bowl gradually empties. It can be seen that as the bowl load reduced, the feed rate increased rapidly. Clearly when the bowl is empty the feed rate will have fallen to zero. For the amplitude setting employed in this test, the bowl could be used to feed the cylindrical parts to a machine or workhead requiring 36 parts per minute. It is clear that, because of the large increase in feed rate as the bowl empties, excessive recirculation of the parts would occur.

II.2 Performance of a Horizontal Delivery Gravity Feed Track

II.2.1 Object

(a) To determine the dynamic coefficient of friction, μ_d, between the parts and feed track used in the experiment.

(b) To examine experimentally and theoretically the performance of a horizontal delivery gravity feed track.

II.2.2 Equipment (a)

The equipment used in the determination of the dynamic coefficient of friction consisted (Fig. II.4) of a straight track whose angle of inclination, θ, to the horizontal could be varied between 20 and 60 degrees. The equipment was designed to record accurately the time taken for a part to slide, from rest, a given distance down the track. Near the top of the track, a short peg projecting upward through a hole in the track retains the part until the spring cantilever supporting the peg is deflected by depressing the button. The deflection of the cantilever also closes a pair of contacts at the moment the part

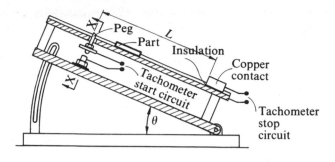

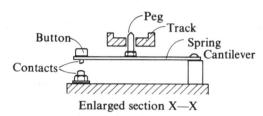

Enlarged section X—X

Figure II.4. Apparatus used in the determination of the dynamic coefficient of friction.

is released; this initiates the count on a digital tachometer. A further contact is positioned at the bottom of the track a distance L from the front of the retaining peg. When the part arrives at the bottom of the track it completes the circuit which stops the count on the tachometer.

II.2.3   Theory (a)

The equation of motion for a part sliding down an inclined track is:

$$m_p a = m_p g \sin \theta - \mu_d m_p g \cos \theta$$

or

$$a/g = \sin \theta - \mu_d \cos \theta \qquad (II.8)$$

Where

m_p = mass of part, lb
θ = track inclination
a = acceleration of part, in/sec^2
μ_d = coefficient of dynamic friction between part and track

For a straight inclined track the acceleration of the part is uniform and the time, t_s, taken for the part to slide a distance L is given by:

$$t_s^2 = 2L/a \tag{II.9}$$

Combining eqs. (II.8) and (II.9) gives:

$$\mu_d = (\sin \theta - 2L/gt_s^2)/\cos \theta \tag{II.10}$$

II.2.4   Procedure (a)

In the present experiment, where the part was of mild steel and the track of aluminium alloy, the times were measured for the part to slide a distance of 4 in. with the track angle set at 30, 45, and 60 degrees. For each condition, 20 readings were taken and averaged, and the 95 per cent confidence limits for each average was computed using the expression $T[S/n_r(n_r - 1)]^{\frac{1}{2}}$ where S is the standard deviation of the sample, n_r is the number of readings in the sample and T is a factor depending on the sample size (when $n_r = 20$, $T = 2.09$). The corresponding values of μ_d were finally computed using eq. (II.10).

II.2.5   Results (a)

The mean values of μ_d obtained for each track angle are presented in Table II.1 together with the corresponding 95 per cent confidence limits. Since no significant variation of μ_d with changes in track angle was evident, it was thought reasonable to take the average of all the readings obtained. This yielded a mean value of $\mu_d = 0.353$ with a range, for 95 per cent confidence, of 0.325 to 0.381.

TABLE II.1

θ, degrees	μ_d	95 per cent confidence limits
30	0.358	± 0.028
45	0.354	± 0.012
60	0.347	± 0.006

II.2.6   Equipment (b)

Figure II.5 shows the design of the experimental horizontal delivery feed track. A parts release and timing arrangement similar to that used in the first part of the experiment is provided. In this case the column of parts is retained by a peg positioned on the

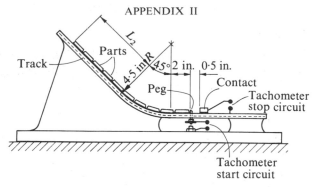

Figure II.5. Apparatus used to investigate the performance of a gravity feed track.

horizontal section 2 in. from the beginning of the curved section and the contact which arrests the column of parts and stops the count is positioned 0·5 in. from the front of the peg.

II.2.7   Theory (b)

The derivation of the theoretical expression for the initial acceleration on release of a column of parts held in a feed track of the present design has already been developed in chapter 6. Thus:

$$a/g = \frac{L_2(\sin \alpha - \mu_d \cos \alpha) - L_1 \mu_d e^{\mu_d \alpha} + [R/(1 + \mu_d^2)] \\ [(1 - \mu_d^2)(e^{\mu_d \alpha} - \cos \alpha) - 2\mu_d \sin \alpha]}{L_2 + L_1 e^{\mu_d \alpha} + (R/\mu_d)(e^{\mu_d \alpha} - 1)}$$

$$(II.11)$$

Substitution of the values of $L_1 = 2$ in., $R = 4·5$ in., and $\alpha = 45$ degrees for the experimental rig and the mean, upper, and lower values of $\mu_d = 0·353$, $0·325$, and $0·381$ respectively, obtained in the first part of the experiment gives the required predicted relationship between a/g and L_2.

In the experiment the time, t_p, was recorded for the column of parts to slide a distance of 0·5 in. Since this distance was small compared with the dimensions of the feed track it could be assumed that the acceleration, a, of the column of parts was constant. Thus:

$$\frac{a}{g} = \frac{2 \times 0·5}{g t_p^2} = \frac{25·9}{(100 t_p)^2} \qquad (II.12)$$

II.2.8   *Procedure (b)*

The time was recorded for the parts to slide 0·5 in. for a range of values of L_2. For each condition an average of 20 readings was obtained.

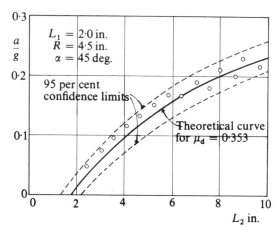

Figure II.6. *Performance of a horizontal delivery gravity feed track (steel parts on aluminium track).*

II.2.9   *Results (b)*

The experimental results are plotted in Fig. II.6 together with the two curves representing the 95 per cent confidence limits. It can be seen that all the experimental results fall within the two theoretical curves representing the 95 per cent confidence limits for the mean value of μ_d.

II.2.10   *Conclusions*

(a) The coefficient of friction between the parts and the track used in the experiment has been successfully determined.

(b) The experimental results obtained for the acceleration of a column of parts in a horizontal delivery gravity feed track fall within the range, for 95 per cent confidence, of predicted values using the results of analysis and the values of μ_d obtained in the first part of the experiment. This confirms that the theory, determined for parts of an infinitesimally small length, is valid for parts of finite length provided that this length is small compared with the dimensions of the track.

(c) The performance of parts in a horizontal delivery gravity feed track can be accurately estimated using the theoretical equation, provided the coefficient of dynamic friction between the parts and the track is known.

Bibliography

AKHMECHET, L. S., BLOKH, O. I., MATSIEYEVSKI, A. G., NESTEROV, Ye. N., and SVIRIDENKO, S. Kh. 'Choice of Parameters for Vibratory Hoppers.' *Machines and Tooling*, 1959, **30**, No. 2, 9.

AKSEL'RAD, E. L. 'Design of Vibratory Feeders.' *Russian Engineering Journal*, 1961, **41**, No. 7, 14.

ANON. 'Analytical Approach Proves that Assembly Machines don't always Cut Costs.' *Metalworking Production*, 1966, **110**, No. 1, 39.

ANON. 'Automation–65.' *The Production Engineer*, 1965, **44**, No. 12, 58.

ANON. *Guide to Work Handling Equipment for Machine Tools and Presses, Part 1—Hoppers and Selector Devices*. P.E.R.A. Report No. 54, Production Engineering Research Association.

ANON. *Hopper Feeds as an Aid to Automation*. Machinery's Yellowback Series No. 39, The Machinery Publishing Co. Ltd.

ANON. 'How Special Diet can reduce Assembly Costs.' *Steel*, 20 July, 1964, 58.

ANON. 'How to Evaluate Automatic Assembly of your Products.' *Steel*, 1961, **148**, No. 8, 66.

ANON. *Vibratory Feeding—The Dynamic Characteristics of Small Parts Feeders.'* P.E.R.A. Report No. 146, Production Engineering Research Association.

BALAKASHIN, B. S. 'Theoretical Problems in the Automation of Assembly Operations.' *Russian Engineering Journal*, 1962, **42**, No. 12, 28.

BALDWIN, S. P. 'How to Make Sure of Easy Assembly.' *Tool and Manufacturing Engineer*, 1966, **56**, No. 5, 76.

BEACHAM, R. C. 'Focus on Automatic Assembly.' *Automation*, 1964, **11**, No. 6, 76.

BEZIER, P. 'The Next Major Step in Automation.' *New Scientist*, 1963, **18**, No. 340, 421.

BOOTH, J. H. and McCALLION, H. 'On Predicting Mean Conveying Velocity of Vibratory Conveyor'. *Proc. I. Mech. E.*, 1963/64, **178**, No. 20, 521.

BOOTHROYD, G. and REDFORD, A. H. 'Free Transfer Can Improve Assembly Machine Economics.' *Metalworking Production*, 1966, **110**, No. 22, 67.

CHARNLEY, C. J. 'Assembly Automation—A Higher Order of Control.' *Mechanical Handling*, 1965, **52**, No. 5, 207.

CUMMINGS, W. C. 'Standardizing Assembly Machines.' *Automation*, 1959, **6**, No. 3, 46.

DE COCK, H. G. 'Vibratory Feeders.' *Phillips Technical Review*, 1962, **24**, No. 3, 84.

DICKINSON, H. D. 'Economic Effects of Automation.' *Engineering*, 1956, **182**, No. 4723, 337.

EMERSON, C. 'Automatic Assembly, Its Potentials and Pitfalls.' *American Machinist*, 1966, **110**, No. 5, 93.

EMERSON, C. 'Primer on Automatic Assembly.' *American Machinist*, 1965, **109**, No. 4, 83.

ESHELMAN, R. H. 'How to Plan Processing Lines for Complete Automation.' *Iron Age*, 1962, **189**, No. 4, 97.

ESKEN, R. 'Automatic Assembly.' *Mechanical Engineering*, 1960, **82**, No. 5, 40.

FOSTER, D. 'Automatic Assembly.' *Control*, 1962, **5**, No. 48, 110.

GITTLER, H. 'Pitfalls to Automation.' *Mass Production*, 1964, **40**, No. 9, 41.

GUTMAN, I. 'Automatic Feeding Devices—Rotary Hoppers.' *Machine Shop Magazine*, May 1960, 265.

GUTMAN, I. 'Vibratory Conveyors.' *Engineer's Digest*, 1963, **24**, No. 5, 93.

GUTMAN, I. 'Vibratory Feeders for Mechanized Work Handling.' *Machinery* 1964, **105**, No. 2716, 1292.

HAWLEY, G. F. *Automating the Manufacturing Process*, 1959. Reinhold Publishing Corpn.

HOLLOWAY, C. C. 'Technical and Economic Aspects Place Accent on Automatic Assembly.' *Automation*, 1963, **10**, No. 12, 50.

HORENBURGER, W. E. 'Sub-assembly Automation Fits a Budget.' *Automation*, 1957, **4**, No. 7, 51.

IREDALE, R. 'The Assembly Machine Comes of Age.' *Metalworking Production*, 15 Sept., 1965, 67.

IREDALE, R. 'Automatic Assembly.' *Metalworking Production*, 1964, (1) 'Present and Future,' 11 March; (2) 'Economic Considerations,' 18 March; (3) 'Engineering the Project,' 25 March; (4) 'Components and Products,' 8 April; (5) 'Feeding and Orientating,' 15 April; (6) 'Machining Features,' 22 April; (7) 'Fastening Methods,' 6 May.

IREDALE, R. 'The Road to Automatic Assembly.' *New Scientist*, 1966, **31**, No. 514, 672.

IRVING, R. R. 'Leave it to Automatic Assembly.' *Iron Age*, 1964, **194**, No. 20, 141.

JENKINS, R. F. 'Why Automatic Assembly?' *Metalworking Production*, 1965, **109**, No. 33, 67.

KAY, J. G. 'Escapements for Automatic Parts Handling.' *Automation*, 1966, **13**, No. 3, 83.

KENDALL, G. H. and HOST, U. A. 'Vibratory Feeding of Parts.' *Automation*, November 1955, 67.

KENDALL, G. H. and WALTER, L. 'Planning Automatic Assembly.' *Engineering*, 1958, **186**, No. 4822, 184.

KRAUS, C. E. 'Chuting and Orientation in Automatic Handling.' *Machine Design*, 1949, 21, No. 9, 95.

KRAUS, C. E. 'Elements of Automatic Handling.' *Machine Design*, November 1951, 142.

La RUE, A. J. 'Stress Quality for Successful Automatic Assembly.' *Automation*, 1960, **7**, No. 6, 73.

LAWSON, A. A., HOMOS, J. A., and TAYTON, R. 'Cards Control Assembly of Components to Circuit Boards.' *Automation*, 1959, **6**, No. 6, 82.

MASON, A. 'Component Design for Mechanised Assembly.' *Machine Shop and Engineering Manufacture*, June 1966, 228 and July 1966, 274.

McKINSEY, W. and MORAN, J. P. 'Application of Vibratory Hopper Feeders.' *The Tool Engineer*, May 1957, 80.

MILLER, M. T. 'Mechanised Feeding of Small Parts.' *Automation*, 1965, **12**, No. 6, 74.

MOSKOWITZ, L. R. 'Types of Vibratory Devices.' *Automation*, December 1958, 69.

MUKHERJEE, S. K. and BASU, S. K. 'An Application of Heuristic Method of Assembly Line Balancing in an Indian Industry.' *Proc. I. Mech. E.*, 1963/64, **178**, No. 11, 277.

MUTSENEK, K. Ya. and LOBZOV, B. A. 'The Reliability and Productivity of Automatic Assembly Machines.' *Russian Engineering Journal*, 1966, **46**, No. 3, 50.

NEKLUTIN, C. N. 'Automation Economics requires Engineered Accounting.' *Automation*, 1957, **4**, No. 11, 38.

NOY, P. C. 'Automatic Assembly—Check Chart for Single-part Complexity.' *Product Engineering*, 31 March, 1958, 124.

PATERSON, R. I. 'Development in Assembly Processes.' *The Production Engineer*, 1965, **44**, No. 6, 304.

PATERSON, R. I. and FOSTER, D. B. 'Automatic Parts Handling.' *Trans. Soc. Instrument Technology*, December 1963, 204.

PAZ, M. 'Conveying Speed of Vibrating Equipment.' 1964. A.S.M.E. Paper No. 64 WA/MH-1.

POVIDAYLO, V. A. 'Design Calculations and Construction of Vibratory Hoppers.' *Machines and Tooling*, 1959, **30**, No. 2, 5.

POVIDAYLO, V. A. 'Optimum Vibratory Feeder Operating Conditions.' *Machines and Tooling*, 1960, **31**, No. 5, 2.

PRENTING, T. O. 'Automatic Assembly—The Economic Considerations.' 1965. A.S.M.E. Paper No. 65-WA/PROD 5.

PRENTING, T. O. 'Parts Handling—Key to Automatic Assembly,' 1965. A.S.T.M.E. Technical Paper No. SP65-136.

PRENTING, T. O. and BATTAGLIN, R. M. 'Precedence Diagram—Tool for Analysis in Assembly Line Balancing.' *J. Industrial Engineering*, 1964, **15**, No. 4, 208.

READER, E. G. 'Handling Small Parts for Assembly.' *Automation*, January 1958, 52.

RILEY, F. J. 'Design of Automatic Assembly Machines.' *Tool and Manufacturing Engineer*, 1962, **48**, No. 5, 91.

RILEY, F. J. 'What Management Should Know about Automatic Assembly Machines.' *Assembly and Fastener Eng.*, 1962, **5**, No. 4, 38, No. 5, 39, No. 6, 29.

ROBERTSON, N. T. 'Controlling Parts Orientation and Flow in Vibratory Bowl Feeders.' *Automation*, 1963, **10**, No. 8, 76.

ROEBUCK, A., CARNEGIE, H. S., and TAYLOR, E. G. 'Mechanical Handling.' *Proc. I. Mech. E.*, 1951, **164**, 113.

SALVESON, M. E. 'The Assembly Line Balancing Problem.' *Trans. A.S.M.E.*, 1955, **77**, 939.

SCHWARTZ, W. 'Twelve Ideas for Design of Feeding, Sorting and Counting Mechanisms.' *Product Engineering*, October 1950, 145.

SIMONE, R. J. 'Standardized Parts Placing Mechanisms Increase Assembly Machine Adaptability.' *Automation*, February 1963, 61.

SIMS, E. R. 'Making Feasibility Studies for Automation.' *Automation*, 1957, **4**, No. 6, 54.

SMITH, F. E. 'Applying Vibratory Bowl-type Feeders.' *Automation*, 1962, **9**, No. 11, 97, **9**, No. 12, 79, **10**, No. 1, 78.

TANIGUCHI, O., SAKATA, M., SUZUKI, Y., and OSANAI, Y. 'Studies on Vibratory Feeder.' *Bull. J.S.M.E.*, 1963, **6**, No. 21, 37.

TIPPING, W. V. 'Mechanized Assembly.' Paper Presented to Soc. of Engineers, 26 April, 1965.

TIPPING, W. V. 'Mechanised Assembly Machines.' (In 20 Parts), *Machine Design Engineering*, June 1965 to January 1967.

TREER, K. R. 'Applying Parts Selectors.' *Automation*, 1957, **4**, No. 7, 40.

TREER, K. R. 'Escapements for Automatic Equipment.' *Automation*, 1957, **4**, No. 2, 80.

TREER, K. R. 'Selecting Intermittent Transfer Devices for Automatic Assembly.' *Automation*, 1962, **9**, No. 12, 61.

WIESE, A. R. 'The Possibilities for Automating Assembly Operations.' *Machinery*, 1964, **105**, No. 2702, 514.

WILBURN, J. E. 'Automatic Assembly Increases Profits.' *Automation*, 1966, **13**, No. 4, 80.

WITTENBERG, G. 'Mechanized Assembly.' *Chartered Mech. Engr.*, 1963, **10**, No. 5, 242.

Index

Inspection; 167, 176, 183.
Intermittent transfer; 8, 10.
In-bowl tooling; 77.
In-line assembly machines; 8, 12.

Jaw escapement; 117.

Limiting conditions for sliding, vibratory bowl feeder; 25, 26.
Load sensitivity of
  centre board hopper; 54.
  external gate hopper; 60.
  reciprocating tube hopper; 48.
  reciprocating fork hopper; 57.
  revolving hook hopper; 69.
  rotary disc feeder; 65.
  vibratory bowl feeder; 35, 36, 40.
Location plungers; 16, 20.

Machine
  life, indexing mechanism; 16, 17.
  pacing; 21.
  rate; 38, 44.
Magazines; 74.
Magnetic
  disc feeder; 72.
  elevating hopper feeder; 73.
Mean conveying velocity, vibratory bowl feeder; 30, 32, 35, 37, 175.
Mechanization of indexing machines; 141.
Mechanized assembly; 5, 8, 36, 77, 117, 126, 128, 141, 147, 148, 150, 151, 154, 155, 156, 161, 164, 171, 180.
Memory pin; 166, 167, 176.

Natural resting aspect; 79, 82.
Nesting parts, re-design of; 161.

Operator; 22, 123, 141, 145, 150, 167, 168, 173, 176, 179, 183.
  assembly; 4, 141, 142, 144, 147.
  pacing; 21.
Orientation, design for
  of nesting parts; 161.
  of studs; 187.
  of truncated cones; 159.
  of washers; 157.

Orienting
  devices; 7, 34, 189.
    active; 77, 78, 80, 83, 87, 175.
    cut-out; 82, 160, 199.
    passive; 77, 83, 86.
    pressure break; 78.
    step device; 83.
    wiper blade; 78.
  of cup-shaped parts; 81, 83, 87.
  of hemispherical parts; 81.
  of parts; 41.
  of rectangular blocks; 81.
  of U-shaped parts; 82.
  of washers; 81.
Out-of-bowl tooling; 77, 87.
Out-of-phase vibratory conveyors; 185.
  optimum phase of; 187.
  phase of; 186.
  track angle of; 187.
  track motion of; 186.

Pacing
  machine; 21.
  operator; 21.
Paddle wheel hopper; 69.
Parts
  buffer stocks of; 108.
  design of; 156.
  natural resting aspect of; 79, 82.
  orienting of; 41, 81, 82, 83, 87.
  placing mechanisms; 7, 90, 119, 175.
    feed track; 117.
    pick and place; 7, 120, 121.
    push and guide; 120.
    rotary index table; 117.
  reduction of; 151.
  quality; 123, 124, 125, 134, 135, 136, 137, 139, 140, 144, 146, 164, 165, 172, 173, 178, 181.
Passive orienting devices; 77, 83, 86.
Pawl type transfer system; 13.
Performance of
  free transfer machines; 128.
  indexing machines; 124.
Phase angle, out-of-phase vibratory conveyor; 186.
Plungers, location; 16, 20.

MADE AND PRINTED IN GREAT BRITAIN BY
J. W. ARROWSMITH LTD., BRISTOL, ENGLAND